Decorated Firearms

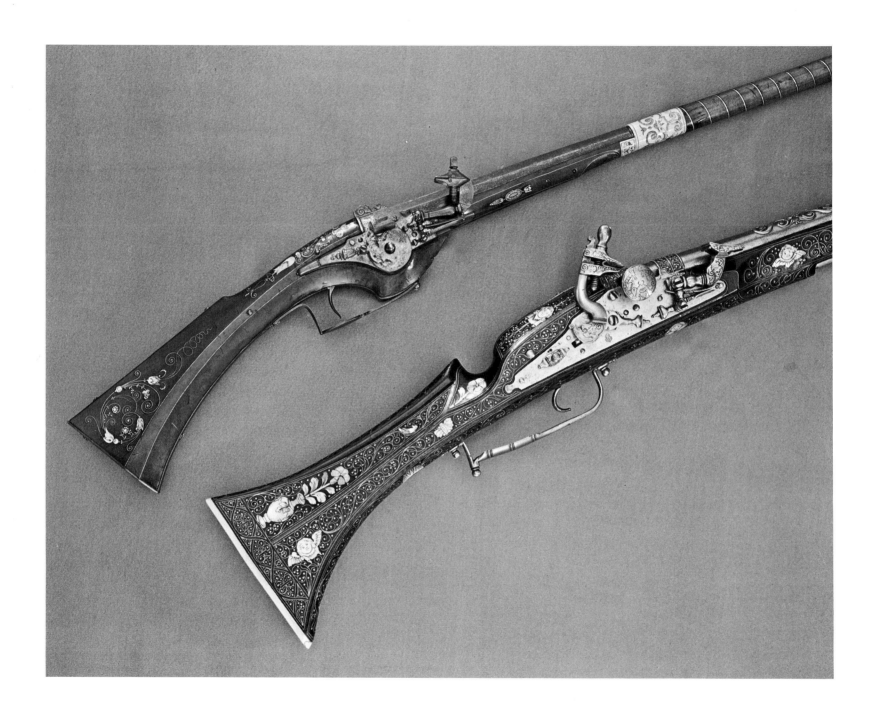

Decorated Firearms

1540-1870

FROM THE COLLECTION OF CLAY P. BEDFORD

By

Wallace B. Gusler *and* James D. Lavin

Published by THE COLONIAL WILLIAMSBURG FOUNDATION
Williamsburg, Virginia

Distributed by THE UNIVERSITY PRESS OF VIRGINIA
Charlottesville, Virginia

© 1977

THE COLONIAL WILLIAMSBURG FOUNDATION

Library of Congress Cataloging in Publication Data

Gusler, Wallace B
  Decorated firearms, 1540–1870, from the Collection of
Clay P. Bedford.

  Bibliography: p. 239
  Includes index.
  1. Firearms—Catalogs. 2. Art metal-work—Catalogs.
3. Bedford, Clay P., 1903–   —Art collections.
I. Lavin, James D., joint author. II. Title.
NK6903.B4G87   739.7′4   76-53750
ISBN 0-87935-041-5

PRINTED IN THE UNITED STATES OF AMERICA

CONTENTS

FOREWORD

FINE FIREARMS, particularly the sporting kind, have traditionally been among the prized possessions of men, including kings, nobles, and provincial gentry. The desire to own a beautifully made gun characterized colonial Virginia gentlemen as much as it did the French and English kings and those in their courts. Of course, the quality of a sporting gun found in Williamsburg in the eighteenth century might differ markedly from that encountered in Paris or London, where the very highest levels of manual skill were employed in shaping and embellishing steel, silver, ivory, and wood to create a harmonious ensemble of graceful form and exquisite decoration that quite belied its ostensible purpose.

Fine firearms have traditionally been very collectible. The *cachet* now attached to a gun that can be proved to have been part of the extraordinary collection (*Cabinet d'Armes*) of Louis XIII proves the point, as much as does the sentiment engendered by "Kentucky" rifles, individually made and decorated in Pennsylvania and Virginia, among other colonies and states, which have often been tenaciously kept by descendants of the original owners.

This exhibition of ninety-four guns (with some additional accessories) from the renowned collection of Clay P. Bedford has been organized by the Colonial Williamsburg Foundation for several reasons. First, guns can be superb examples of the decorative arts of a period—although too often omitted from any discussion of the subject—and we have been accumulating and exhibiting remarkable collections of decorative arts for fifty years. Indeed, our future plans call for an expansion of our offerings in the decorative arts. Most of the firearms exhibited and catalogued here were made in the period spanned by colonial Williamsburg.

Second, the craftsmanship involved in the making of virtually all these guns directly relates to an aspect of our educational activities that is outstanding—one of the most ambitious crafts programs in existence today. Here we have men casting and forging iron and steel, silver and brass, engraving metal, and carving wood in the manner of the seventeenth- and eighteenth-century craftsmen who made the memorable objects in this exhibition.

Third, these firearms bear directly on an important aspect of our historical mission—to reveal how society in this part of the New World modeled itself upon and departed from its parental stock in the Old World, and how civilized and civilizing ideas spread through Europe and into America in the years between settlement and revolution. Fine guns reveal more clearly than many areas of the decorative arts the radiation outward from Paris of style and motif as well as technology, the continuing changes of fashion (sometimes almost feverish in their pace), and the absorption into the English fabric of French innovations which then became interwoven, however distantly, into the American.

Without the perceptiveness, enthusiasm, and generosity of Clay P. Bedford it would have been impossible to have had this exhibition or its catalogue. Colonial Williamsburg and its many friends owe him a great debt of gratitude. Mr. Bedford undertook the difficult task of choosing the guns to exhibit—less than one-tenth of an encyclopedic collection, assembled in the amazingly short period of a decade. Any collector will know what agonized decisions were involved in that process. Mr. Bedford also supplied some of the information for the catalogue, together with Stephen V. Grancsay, curator emeritus of arms and armor, the Metropolitan Museum of Art, New York. Furthermore, Mr. Bedford most generously enabled us to produce a catalogue that was written and designed to do proper justice to the importance and quality of the guns.

We were doubly fortunate to have in Williamsburg two such authorities on firearms as Wallace B. Gusler, curator of furniture at Colonial Williamsburg and formerly master gunsmith; and James D. Lavin, associate professor of romance languages at the College of William and Mary and author of two monographs on European firearms. We believe that new and significant observations have been made herein, again provoked by the quality of the objects. All the photographs were supplied by Richard Dietrich of Phoenix, Arizona.

Finally, we must thank another Williamsburg resident, Thomas W. Wood, for his help and advice in acting as liaison between this museum and the founder of one of the finest private collections of firearms in existence today.

GRAHAM HOOD
Director of Collections

Short Title List

BLAIR, *Pistols*
    Claude Blair. *Pistols of the World*. New York: Viking Press, 1968.

HAYWARD, *Gunmaker*
    John Forrest Hayward. *The Art of the Gunmaker*. 2 vols. New York: St. Martin's Press, 1962–1963.

HOFF, *Feuerwaffen*
    Arne Hoff. *Feuerwaffen*. 2 vols. Braunschweig: Klinkhardt & Biermann, 1969.

LENK, *Flintlock*
    Torsten Lenk. *The Flintlock: its origin and development*. Translated by G. A. Urquart; edited by J. F. Hayward. London: Holland Press Ltd., 1965.

SCHEDELMANN, *Die grossen Büchsenmacher*
    Hans Schedelmann. *Die grossen Büchsenmacher*. Braunschweig: Klinkhardt & Biermann, 1972.

PREFACE

THE NINETY-FOUR FIREARMS selected for this publication were chosen primarily because of their artistic qualities. They are the products of various European nations and the United States and represent three centuries of artistic development. Consequently, this book, dependent upon the materials in the collection, is not intended to be a history of firearms. However, certain arms included here shed new light on previously accepted concepts. In regard to them, we have carefully studied the examples at hand, related arms, and documentation in order to arrive at our conclusions. In the majority of cases, we have explained the reasons for the dates we have assigned; in these explanations, usually only major dating factors are cited, since more detailed explanations were deemed impractical when the major details were sufficient.

In the majority of entries we have adhered to the following format: the description of the arm—stock, barrel, lock, mounts; discussion of the maker; an analysis of the arm in the context of its period and region; its provenance and dimensions.

France was chosen as the first national group since French design had the greatest international influence, and is often referred to in regard to many arms in the succeeding categories. In some cases, we have formed national groupings not according to modern political boundaries, but rather according to cultural affinity. An introduction to these groupings is given where there are sufficient arms to warrant it.

We have also introduced a new terminology for stockwoods. An illustrated discussion is included as an appendix.

THE impressive group of French firearms that follows spans two and one-half centuries and illustrates the artistic and mechanical development of European firearms during the period 1600–1845. The French were the first to publish gunsmiths' designs that originated in the workshops of leading artisans. Not only did these designs illustrate academic ornament, but they also were engraved actual size so that the printed sheets provided precise patterns for gunmakers working far beyond the borders of France. These pattern books tended to consolidate Western European firearms design, especially in the case of applied ornament. With the French development of the flintlock, and the series of designs adapted to its evolving forms, French dominance in firearms design was well established by the mid-seventeenth century.

Before the 1640s France exerted little influence over the arms of neighboring countries, but by mid-century French designs had gained popularity abroad. From that time on, Paris was the center of stylistic evolution, and Parisian style developed rapidly and was extremely sensitive to change. This sensitivity was so marked that the life of a style might span no more than a single decade. At the same time this inventive vitality does not seem to have penetrated either the provinces or outside France, where the acceptance of Parisian design was neither immediate nor universal. Regional or national styles often persisted in combination with Parisian elements, which sometimes continued to be used as much as a half-century after their abandonment in Paris. Consequently, provincial and foreign arms require careful scrutiny in order

to determine their most modern feature, before which, despite their overall appearance, they cannot be dated. In some cases where regional styles were very deeply entrenched, even this method must be used with caution.

The earliest French example pictured here is a wheel-lock pistol of ca. 1600. Artistically it continues the tradition of the second half of the sixteenth century in retaining the crowded composition of mother-of-pearl and brass wire stock inlay. More elaborate arms of this period are heavily chiseled on their locks and barrels, which are often further enhanced by gilding. Considered overall, these French arms are quite akin to their Germanic counterparts. This style, in vogue during the latter half of the sixteenth century, virtually disappeared during the early years of the seventeenth. By about 1615 at least two new French schools had evolved, both of which eschewed the highly decorated stock.

The first centered around Metz and may be designated the Lorraine school. It retained the sixteenth-century tradition of sculptural elements, but underwent intense refinement; the relief chiseling became limited to specific areas generally concentrated on the dog, wheel retainer, pancover, and the tail of the lockplate. The sculpture is usually of the highest quality and is accented by the flat planes of the lock surface. It may be further emphasized by fine engraving composed of small elements covering these surfaces. Stocking became lighter and graceful, inlay more open, and small amounts of engraved metal sheet, wire, and nails decorative in cross section replaced the earlier maze of engraved staghorn and mother-of-pearl.

The other school appeared almost simultaneously in Normandy and initially seems to have been restricted to Lisieux. Its most characteristic feature is its austere approach. Lock decoration is often restricted only to turnings, while barrels and iron mounts may exhibit damascened designs of stylized foliage. In contrast to the decoration of the metal parts of the Lorraine school firearms, the chief decorative feature of Lisieux arms is the stock, whose form and applied ornament show great variety. However, in general, the stock inlay is more sparse than that of Metz and retains mother-of-pearl, staghorn, wire, and nail elements to a lesser degree.

The coexistence of these two schools is substantiated by the *Cabinet d'Armes* of Louis XIII, the inventory of which includes numerous arms from both schools. This inventory was not begun until the third quarter of the seventeenth century, during the reign of Louis XIV. Despite being compiled more than a generation after the appearance of some weapons in the royal collection, the inventory provides the closest extant references to them. Completed on February 20, 1673, it listed 337 objects and was subsequently revised to include additional items. At the time of the first inventory the arms were stamped with the inventory numbers, normally on the underside of the stock just forward of the triggerguard. A surprising number of the arms have survived, two of which are illustrated in this book. Existing examples make it evident that the numbering was at random and had no chronological basis.

The importance of the inventory to the study of French arms cannot be overstated. It well documents Louis XIII's patronage of the Lorraine and Lisieux schools and his acquisition of arms from other areas of France. His patronage tended to consolidate divergent French styles as well as attracting to the capital their provincial makers and designers. Outstanding among them were Marin le Bourgeois, François du Clos, and Thomas Picquot, to whom Louis awarded *logement* under the "grand galerie du Louvre."

It has been long recognized that the flintlock originated in France, and most of the earliest examples come from the *Cabinet d'Armes*. Bourgeois, du Clos, and Picquot are the names most immediately associated with the earliest documentable flintlocks. The origin and development of this system will be dealt with in the next section.

Following the flintlock's general acceptance, numerous series of published patterns were issued illustrating its mechanical and artistic development. Using these patterns in conjunction with dated arms, Dr. Torsten Lenk has identified and named French firearms styles. Lenk's nomenclature is used throughout this work. In chronological order, the styles are:

Date	Style	Printed Source
1640s	Western Europe	Several plates from François Marcou, Paris, 1657, are the only pattern book representations of this style.
1650s–1660s	Thuraine and le Hollandois	C. Jacquinet, Paris, 1660, and Jean Bérain, Paris, 1659.
1670–1700	Classical Louis XIV	Claude Simonin, Paris, 1684 (1685), and Claude and Jacques Simonin, Paris, 1693.
1695–1735	"Bérain"	De la Collombe, Paris, 1702–1705, four sheets appended to the 1705 reissue of Claude Simonin's 1684 patterns. Nicolas Guérard, Paris, early eighteenth century. De la Collombe, Paris, 1738.
1735–1790	Louis XV (rococo)	De Marteau, Paris, mid-eighteenth century (two plates dated 1743 and 1749).
1790–1825	Empire	J. F. Lucas, Paris?, plates dated 1807 and 1808.

The invention of the flintlock has been attributed to Marin le Bourgeois. In his monumental work *The Flintlock*, Dr. Torsten Lenk first defined this mechanism and distinguished it from other snaplocks that used flint and steel.[1] Lenk very tentatively suggested that the inventor of the flintlock may have been Marin le Bourgeois, but he appears more firmly convinced that it originated in Lisieux prior to 1615.[2] As Lenk defined it, the flintlock has a fully internal sear which pivots vertically to engage a tumbler that is notched for both full- and half-cock. It must also have a combined battery and pancover. This has become the standard definition, and it is used throughout this book. Since the publication of Lenk's work in 1939, considerable information has come to light concerning Marin le Bourgeois's role in the "invention" of the flintlock and the time of its appearance.

Dr. Lenk's thesis is based on the signature M. LE BOVRGEOIS A LISIEVL that appears on what he believed to be the earliest extant flintlock arm, now in Leningrad's Hermitage Museum (No. 94). His dating of this gun resulted from its close affinity to another early flintlock gun that he attributed to Marin's brother Jean le Bourgeois, who died in 1615. This second gun, formerly in the Renwick Collection, was recently acquired by the Metropolitan Museum of Art.[3] Lenk based his attribution to Jean le Bourgeois on its barrel stamp, a crossbow in a circle flanked by what he thought to be the initials IB. The stock of the Metropolitan gun has the monogram of Louis XIII, who acceded to the throne in 1610, which appeared to provide it with a bracket date of 1610–1615. Lenk was further influenced by the fact that Marin le

Bourgeois presented a hunting bugle, crossbow, and gun to Henri IV in 1605. He would like to identify the latter as the gun now in the Hermitage Museum.

Lenk's theory remained unassailable until Sir James Mann published the Wallace Collection Catalogues in 1962. Describing the wheel-lock pistol (No. 1110) that was also illustrated by Lenk, who attributed it to Jean le Bourgeois on the basis of its mark, Mann pointed out that the crossbow was flanked not by the initials IB, as Lenk believed, but rather by PB. In describing the gun subsequently bought by the Metropolitan Museum—the very flintlock gun on which Lenk's argument hinged—the 1972 Sotheby's catalogue reveals that the barrel mark, given as IB by Lenk, was also in reality PB. The same catalogue carries the Bourgeois attribution further by ascribing this mark to Pierre, brother of Marin and Jean, who died in 1627. Assuming that these marks are correctly attributed to the Bourgeois family, this changes the terminus ad quem of the Lisieux flintlocks to at least 1627 since it is now recognized that there are no flintlock arms with the IB mark on their barrels. The wheel-lock gun from the *Cabinet d'Armes* illustrated here (No. 2) also has the PB mark on its barrel; Pierre le Bourgeois will be discussed further in connection with it.

As can be seen, Lenk's conclusions, admittedly tentative, on the origin of the flintlock are no longer valid, and the corpus of existing evidence must be reevaluated. His hypothesis has been given further credence by successive writers who lacked Lenk's caution. The reexamination of the flintlock's genesis in France is a monumental task that requires considerable documentary research, and our objective in this brief work can be no more than to shed light on the problem and point the way toward a possible solution. Therefore, we must consider again the role of Marin le Bourgeois.

"*Vallet de chambre*" to Henri IV from 1598 to 1633, Marin le Bourgeois seems to have been a man of many parts. He

---

[1] The English translation of Chap. 3 of Lenk's work dealing with this subject is difficult to research. The numeration of the footnotes in the text is hopelessly out of register with the notes at the end of the chapter.

[2] Lenk, *Flintlock*, p. 37.

[3] Sotheby, November 21, 1972, lot 21.

first appears as a painter working on decorations to celebrate the entry of the Duc de Joyeuse into Lisieux in 1583. He is referred to as a gunsmith only once when, in 1605, he is recorded as traveling from Lisieux to Paris to deliver a gun, hunting bugle, and crossbow, "all of his own invention," to Henri IV. Possibly as a result of this presentation he received his "*brevet de logement*" among other artists in the Louvre Galleries in 1608. He was referred to in his *brevet* as "painter, valet, worker in movable globes, sculptor, and other mechanical inventions." He received his pay through 1633 and died the next year.[4]

Only two existing firearms with a full Bourgeois signature are known. Both are by Marin. One is the Hermitage Museum gun mentioned previously; the other is in the Musée de l'Armée, Paris (No. M.435). The former is signed on a decorative bronze strap that encircles the stock, the latter on the buttplate. Neither has a mark on its lock or barrel. A comparison of these two guns with the one in the Metropolitan Museum having the PB barrel mark reveals that the damascening of the barrel of the Metropolitan gun is markedly different in design and quality from that of the two guns signed by Marin. The decoration on both is composed of continuous, flowing lines of foliage, while on the Metropolitan example it is more geometrical and contains straight lines. Significantly, the design on the barrel of the Metropolitan gun virtually repeats the decorative vocabulary of its wire stock inlay. These same design elements are also repeated on the stock of the Hermitage gun bearing Marin's signature, but here they are not related to its barrel decoration. The obvious conclusion is that both arms were stocked by the same master, but that Marin decorated the mounts and barrel of the Hermitage gun as he probably did on the gun in the Musée de l'Armée. The damascening of the two guns directly

associated with his signature is so markedly superior that one can easily accept it as resulting from his involvement in Parisian art. On the other hand, the damascening on the Metropolitan PB gun is, by comparison, believeable as provincial work. Marin's signature, which appears only on gun mounts, serves to confirm that he was a decorator and possibly a mounts maker. Further supporting this contention is another flintlock gun in the Musée de l'Armée (Lenk, *Flintlock*, pl. 11, nos. 1 and 2) whose unsigned mounts and barrel apparently were decorated by Marin, but its lock is marked by another marker whose initials appear to be IC.

In spite of the single reference in 1605 to Marin le Bourgeois as "gunsmith," the evidence is overwhelming that he was an artist and sculptor, and, in fact, he received his *logement* in the Louvre on this basis. He participated in the making of firearms probably only as a decorator, and the guns on which he worked—including the one he presented to Henri IV—most likely were produced by an unknown gunsmith or smiths under contract to him. This practice was certainly not uncommon in seventeenth-century France.[5]

On the basis of its lock form, Dr. Lenk considered the Hermitage Bourgeois gun to be the earliest flintlock known. The Metropolitan gun, however, appears more archaic in two respects, the more important of which is the position of the battery spring along the lower edge of the plate rather than in the middle as on the two Marin le Bourgeois examples. This lower mounting retains the position of the dog spring of wheel-locks. Second, the bent tip of the mainspring that bears against the tumbler is much more archaic than those of the two guns having Marin's signature and seems to indicate that the Metropolitan gun is the earliest of the Lisieux flintlocks. Since, as has been seen, the Metropolitan gun does not show the hand of Marin le Bourgeois, it appears

---

[4] Lenk, *Flintlock*, pp. 20–30, provides the various sources for this information.

[5] Hayward, *Gunmaker*, I, pp. 138–139.

[4]

to remove his two signed guns for the moment from the running as the earliest of the flintlocks and weakens the attribution of the invention to him.

All surviving examples of the earliest flintlocks appear closely related and share such features as an external cock buffer, a very straight-necked cock, and a lockplate with a pronounced bulge in its lower profile that obviously derives from the wheel-lock. The earliest identifiable flintlocks—the Metropolitan and Hermitage guns—have short, thick batteries with separate, screwed-on striking faces. The distance from their pivot screw to the rear edge of the pancover is greater than the height of their striking surface. A relic of the snaphaunce battery, this proportion appears common to all the earliest flintlocks. However, apart from these two guns, there are no further flintlocks having the separate battery face. Another short-lived feature was the trigger with its pivot pin above the top edge of the lockplate, an obvious surviving element of the wheel- and snaphaunce locks. It had disappeared by the early 1630s as proved by the second Marin le Bourgeois gun (Musée de l'Armée, M.435). The barrels of these early flintlocks have slightly flanged moldings at the breech, or none at all, and are fitted with simple slotted rear sights. These elements are vestigial survivals of the wheel-lock's heavy turned and flanged moldings and the large slotted rear sight of ogee profile (see Nos. 1 and 2).

Circumstantial evidence and a number of surviving arms point to Lisieux as the probable origin of the flintlock. However, other examples showing these primitive features, many of which were pictured by Lenk (*Flintlock*, pls. 14–15), should not be overlooked. Most notable is the gun in Windsor Castle (No. 316) signed *Faict A Turene* on its lockplate and dated 1630 on its lower beveled edge.[6] Although made in the south of France, its lock ornament is characteristic of

⁶ Howard L. Blackmore, *Royal Sporting Guns at Windsor* (London: H. M. Stationery Office, 1968), pl. 22.

the Lorraine school and may represent the work of a transplanted gunsmith. Its plate is more closely related to the wheel-lock than are the foregoing examples; its cock is equally straight; and while the battery is missing, the distance of its screw hole from the pan suggests that it was of the long pivot, short striking surface form. This lock and some of the features of the stock are closely related to the wheel-lock gun signed *Jean Henequin a metz* on the lock and barrel, which is dated 1621. A flintlock gun quite similar to the Turenne is depicted in the portrait of the Earl of Denbigh in the National Gallery, London. The portrait is attributed to Van Dyck, and if this is correct, it must have been painted during his second residence in England, from late 1635 to his death in 1641. In any event, Sir William Feilding became first Earl of Denbigh on September 14, 1622, dying on April 8, 1643. It would thus appear that the Turenne gun represents an earlier stage in the development of the flintlock than does the one in the Metropolitan; moreover, its lock development is somewhat more archaic, and its barrel breech moldings are of the earlier wheel-lock type. Also pictured by Lenk (*Flintlock*, pls. 14–15) are three early flintlock guns from the *Cabinet d'Armes* having similar stocks with butt-traps that relate them to Alsace and Lorraine. Their locks embody many of the early flintlock features mentioned above, and, in conjunction with cock patterns by Jean Henequin of Metz engraved in the 1620s (Lenk, *Flintlock*, pl. 103, nos. 1 and 3), they show that the Lorraine school was one of the earliest centers of flintlock production.

The first documentary proof of the flintlock's existence are the 1630 Turenne gun already mentioned; two engravings by Philippe Cordier, both dated 1635; and a dated flintlock gun by François du Clos dated 1636 (Musée de l'Armée, M.410). To this evidence may be added the woodcuts of lockplates and cocks by Thomas Picquot of Lisieux, who published his series of designs in Paris in 1638. Studied as a whole, this material reveals that the lock of the du Clos arm is of a much more highly developed form than are those in the two series of patterns, while the lock of the Turenne gun is more archaic. That the locks shown by Picquot in 1638 are more archaic than those illustrated by Cordier in 1635 is particularly noticeable in the evolution of the S-shaped cock. Since published patterns are normally a retrospective compilation of designs, this chronological discrepancy between the two pattern books, as well as the 1636 du Clos arm, is to be expected. Using the du Clos gun as a basis to reconstruct their chronology, the Picquot patterns are the oldest, followed by the Cordier designs, and then the du Clos gun.

By this dating method, we are able to date the Musée de l'Armée Marin le Bourgeois gun (M.435), whose flintlock very closely resembles those from the early 1630s depicted by Picquot, to shortly before Marin's death in 1634. This close relationship to Picquot can be seen in the cock and the pointed ends of the lockplate. However, its plate is more advanced since the top edge behind the pan lacks the earlier downward drop and is straighter in profile. Furthermore, its internal battery spring relates it to the Picquot and Cordier patterns and the du Clos gun, all from the 1630s. The Hermitage Marin le Bourgeois flintlock would then appear to be from the late 1620s. The cast and chased classical bust on its stock, which is almost identical to that of the 1636 du Clos gun, certainly confirms this dating. While differing in fine chased details, the two castings appear to have been produced from the same casting pattern. Without question, the Hermitage Bourgeois and the du Clos guns, both made for Louis XIII, are arms of the highest fashion whose unconventional artistic design is quite similar. To accept, as has been previously presented, that more than a quarter-century separates the use of the same casting pattern to create virtually the same fashion for the same individual, is unbelievable. Fur-

thermore, the Hermitage gun's association with the Metropolitan flintlock gun marked PB on the barrel certainly supports the 1620s date assigned to it, providing the attribution of this mark to Pierre le Bourgeois is correct.

The flintlock's appearance in the 1620s would certainly place in more logical perspective the gunsmith François Poumerol's 1631 poem to Louis XIII in which he extols the virtues of the snaphaunce over the "new" flintlock.[7] The subject of the *"fuzil nouveau"* could hardly have warranted Poumerol's argument to the king had not the flintlock at that time been considered a novelty.[8]

In view of the evidence at hand, it is not realistic to conclude that the flintlock made its appearance in France at any time other than the third decade of the seventeenth century.

---

[7] Lenk, *Flintlock*, pp. 28–29, quotes the relevant stanzas of the poem.

[8] This poem accompanied Poumerol's presentation of a gun to the king. Lenk interprets the poem to mean that the arm was a snaphaunce. However, a careful reading of the verses seems to indicate that the presentation gun was actually a flintlock.

Simonin In et Fecit

1 *Wheel-lock Holster Pistol*

FRENCH, ca. 1600

THE round barrel tapers from breech to muzzle, where it terminates in a reinforced turning. The breech has two strong round moldings that are larger in diameter than the remainder of the barrel. Immediately forward is the maker's intaglio stamp, DG (Støckel 2366, Metz), surrounded by foliate engraving that continues, intermixed with strapwork, for about three inches. The lock is stamped with the initials IP over a star. As is usual in French wheel-locks, the wheel arbor pivots in the iron sideplate opposite the lock, and an iron pin passes through the wrist about an inch behind the lockplate to secure the mainspring. In this example the lockplate terminates in an acorn, and the half wheelcover represents a dolphin. Brass wire divides the walnut stock into panels containing engraved mother-of-pearl plaques and inlays shaped like fantastic creatures on a ground of fine brass wire, brass stars, and small mother-of-pearl leaves. The stock terminates in an engraved horn tip (replaced) at the muzzle, and is fitted with a simple iron triggerguard and a support plate beneath the lock. The fluted brass ramrod pipe and the engraved horn ramrod entry plate are replacements.

Claude Blair has noted a very similar pistol in two portraits of Sir Anthony Mildmay (d. 1617), who may have acquired them when he served as ambassador to France in 1596–1597.[1] A closely related pistol, possibly from the same workshop, is in the Victoria and Albert Museum (M.488–1927).

Provenance: Geoffrey Jenkinson, London, 1968.
Overall length, 32 in. (81.2 cm.); barrel, 24¼ in. (61.5 cm.); caliber, .37

---

[1] Blair, *Pistols*, p. 91.

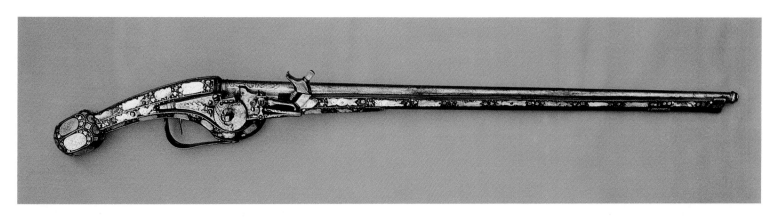

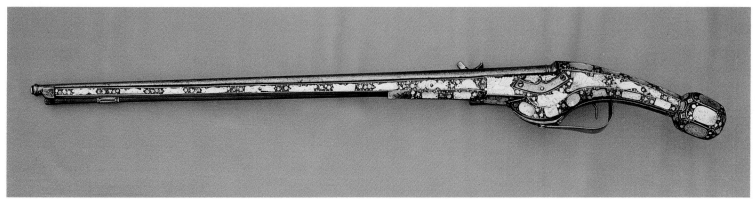

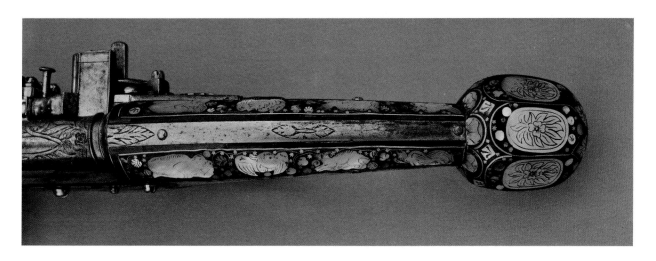

2 *Wheel-lock Fowling Piece*

FRENCH (LISIEUX), ca. 1615

THE fruitwood two-piece full stock is inlaid with engraved brass and silver wire leaves, borders, and volutes, and engraved mother-of-pearl masks, husks, and leaves that have small buds and flower centers of green-dyed ivory. Engraved ivory bands surround the barrel and forestock at both ends, and the wood is wrapped spirally with an inlaid silver wire. The number 93 is stamped in the stock just forward of the triggerguard.

The barrel is made of two sections screwed together. The short round breech section is gilded and has a flanged ring turning. The remainder of the breech is octagonal, terminating at its juncture with the round front section, which is completely sheathed by the forestock. An engraved slotted rear sight is attached to the extreme breech, and the round makers mark—a crossbow flanked by the initials P.B.—is struck in the top facet.[1] The iron barrel tang extends from the barrel breech completely over the comb of the stock and ends touching the iron buttplate.

The wheel-lock of French construction is fitted with an external wheel whose retainer is chiseled in the form of a winged dragon or wyvern secured to the plate through its urn-shaped finial. It has a push-button pancover release, and a bridle connects the dog and dogspring retaining screws. The simple iron triggerguard with a single piercing is attached by two screws entering the floorplate that extends from the bottom of the keel to the butt.

The stock of this gun bears the stamped inventory number 93 of the *Cabinet d'Armes* from the general inventory of the "Mobilier de la Couronne sous Louis XIV" completed in 1673. In the transcription of 1729 it is described as

> An arquebus of one foot 10 inches, the barrel with eight flats, blued gilded at the breech, together with its wheel-lock, having a gilded dragon on the wheel, mounted on a stock of sorb-apple ornamented with flowers of copper, silver and mother-of-pearl; the said arquebus, long with its barrel extension, 3 feet 8 inches.

The extremely long barrel extension is this gun's most distinctive feature. Its function is unclear, however, since a long series of threads makes its expedient removal for loading impractical. This unusual construction has been explained as permitting the gun to serve the dual function of arquebus and pistol. While indeed possible, it leaves unexplained the curious sheathing of the barrel section, and internal threads at the extreme muzzle. Moreover, two drilled holes in the ivory transitional band obviously were intended for a purpose equally inexplicable. Considered separately, the detached barrel appears curiously like an ivory-tipped walking stick. Several examples of similar construction are known, the earliest of which appears to be the French wheel-lock gun in the Skokloster Collection, Sweden.[2]

The only mark on this gun is the PB and crossbow struck in the barrel breech. On November 21, 1972, an early flintlock gun, also from the *Cabinet d'Armes*, bearing the same

---

[1] This is reproduced only in Wallace Collection Catalogues, *European Arms and Armour*, ed. Sir James Mann. II: *Arms* (London: Printed for the Trustees by William Clowes and Sons, Ltd., 1962), p. 519.

[2] Hoff, *Feuerwaffen*, I, pp. 88–89, pl. 72.

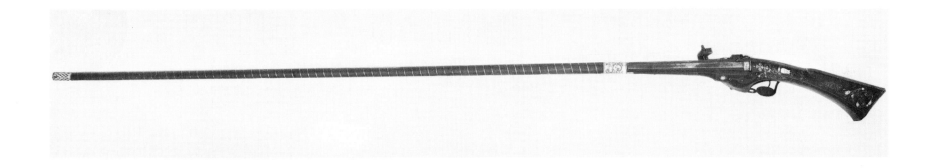

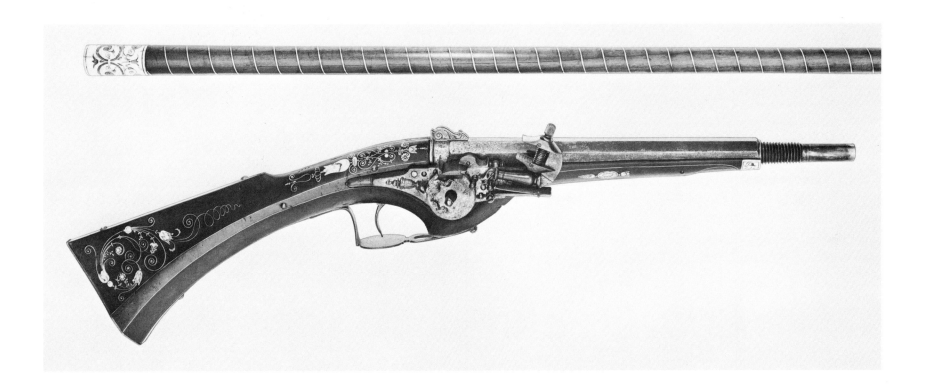

P.B. stamp on the underside of the barrel was bought by the Metropolitan Museum of Art, New York. Sotheby's catalogue of the sale attributes the mark to Pierre le Bourgeois of Lisieux, brother of Marin and Jean, and gives the date of his death as 1627.[3] None of the works in the accompanying bibliography gives the source for this statement. John Hayward's 1973 article in the *Journal of the Royal Armoury*,[4] Stockholm, states that Pierre is recorded as a gunsmith in the Lisieux archives, but cites neither document nor date.

M. Jean Feret of Lisieux subsequently provided us with a photocopy from the register of the "actes de décès" for the year 1627, which relates the burial on October 8, 1627, of a Pierre le Bourgeois of the parish of St. Germain in Lisieux.[5] Neither his occupation nor his date of birth is mentioned in the entry. In the marriage contract of the daughter of Jean le Bourgeois, deceased, dated coincidentally 1627, Jean is referred to as "master armorer and clockmaker."[6] M. Georges Huard, who apparently traces his descent from the Bourgeois family of Lisieux, in 1934 published a family genealogy in *Étude de Topographie lexovienne*.[7] In it he lists Pierre, Jean, and Marin le Bourgeois as brothers, giving the dates of their deaths as 1627, 1615, and 1634 respectively. Of the three, Marin was by far the best known. The existence of gun mounts signed by Marin, the contemporary reference to Jean as "armurier," and the coincidence of initials in the IB and PB barrel marks are the relatively strong circumstancial evidence that has led to the attribution of the PB mark to Pierre le Bourgeois, who is not documented as having been a gunmaker. This attribution is further supported by the strong similarity of decoration between this wheel-lock gun and the Leningrad flintlock gun bearing Marin's signature on its stock.

As discussed in the introduction, characteristics of the earliest recognizable arms coming from the Lisieux school may be seen in the wheel-lock gun illustrated here. Significant dating features are the strongly tapered barrel still retaining its higher flanged molding at the breech and the large slotted rear sight of ogee profile. On the lock, there are the sculptural wheel retainer and the boldly contoured dog neck as well as the strong crisp turnings of the wheel retainer and pancover finials and the dog bridle.

Provenance: Sotheby (Langton Hall Collection), November 30, 1962, lot 201; Sotheby, July 23, 1973, lot 59.
Overall length with barrel extension, 67½ in. (171.5 cm.); barrel without extension, 9¾ in. (24.7 cm.); barrel extension, 46¼ in. (117.5 cm.); caliber, .45

---

[3] Sotheby, Sale Catalogue, November 21, 1972, lot 21 (pp. 28–31).
[4] A typescript of this article was supplied by Dr. Arne Hoff, Copenhagen.
[5] Personal communication from M. Jean Feret, May 31, 1976.
[6] Lenk, *Flintlock*, p. 30.
[7] Georges Huard, *Étude de Topographie lexovienne* (Paris: Jouve & Cie., 1934), n.p.

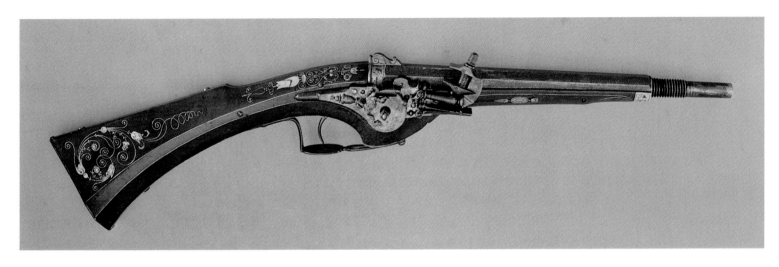

2

3 Snaphaunce Gun

FRENCH, dated 1622 (ca. 1630)

THE fruitwood full stock, inlaid with engraved plaques of mother-of-pearl, ends in a bone buttplate. Both the buttplate and several of the inlays are restorations, most notably the shield and ax opposite the lock. On the underside, just forward of the triggerguard, is stamped the number 130. Brass wire borders enclose silver wire volutes interspersed with inlaid brass stars. The round barrel, tapered and flared at the muzzle, is decorated with six iron bands, four double and two single, which are relief chiseled and are bordered with silver beads. Four iron serpents in high relief surrounding a small satyr are chiseled midway between the two rearmost sets of rings. Forward of these a silver medial bead extends to the band at the muzzle where the flared portion is relief chiseled with naturalistic leaves above a punched ground. A raised ring at the breech is notched to form the rear sight; the front sight is a silver bead. The snaphaunce lock of English type is lightly engraved with foliage and grotesque masks. The date 1622 is engraved on the pancover, and the maker's mark—a shield containing the initials HB under an armored helmet (Støckel 2778)—is struck on the plate below the cock buffer. A sliding manual safety is mounted on the lockplate behind the cock. The iron triggerguard has filed moldings and a ball finial at the rear.

The stock of this gun bears the stamped inventory number 130 of the *Cabinet d'Armes*, which formed part of the general inventory of the "Mobilier de la Couronne" ordered by Louis XIV and completed in 1673. The majority of the arms represented in this inventory were those that had belonged to Louis XIII, among which this piece undoubtedly figures.

The 1729 transcription of the *Cabinet d'Armes* inventory for this gun reads:

> A fusil in the English style, of 3 feet 10 inches, the barrel round whose muzzle is hatched, enriched with six moldings with inlaid silver, chiseled with four serpents and a small Satyr in relief; the lock mounted on a blackened stock enriched with copper and silver wire and copper dots and with trophies beasts and birds of mother-of-pearl inlaid, and two pots of flowers likewise of mother-of-pearl on the butt, and engraved on the pancover 1622.[1]

It has recently been disputed whether this piece is of English or French manufacture. In fact, it appears to embody elements of both, which probably explains the inventory reference to "a fusil in the English style." There appears to be little doubt that the lock and triggerguard are indeed English and contemporaneous. The stock and barrel are French in both quality and decoration, but they have been manufactured in an apparent conscious attempt to imitate English form. While there is no known identical parallel to this barrel, it exhibits many decorative characteristics of contemporary French arms. The raised and chiseled iron bands may appear unusual, but their inlaid silver beading is very reminiscent of similarly inlaid barrels on a large series of flintlock guns from the 1630s and 1640s classified by Lenk as Western European.

Many of these Western European guns have designs utilized by Paris gunsmiths, and undoubtedly the majority are

---

[1] Lenk, *Flintlock*, p. 171.

[14]

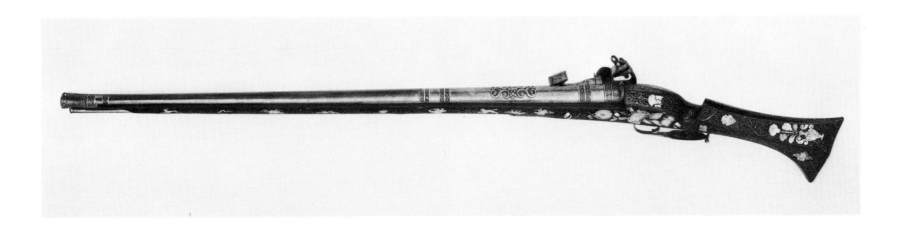

of French manufacture. Their barrels are characterized by heavy chiseling nearly always separated by a series of three or four relief rings edged with tiny beads. A longitudinal central bead occasionally further divides the heavy ornament of the breech and at times extends forward to the muzzle in the manner of a sighting rib. While lacking the profusion of high relief chiseling of the Western Europe group, the design of the barrel of this gun utilizes the basic elements of this formula: the division of the barrel by a series of beaded bands; the beaded sighting rib, here executed in silver; and the sculptured chiseled elements. Replacing the overall chiseling of the breech is a single boldly executed design relating directly to this flintlock group, but which in its superior quality is more akin to the sculptural elements of contemporary French wheel-locks. However, its design elements—satyr, volutes, and S-shaped serpents attacking themselves[2]—are all taken directly from Lenk's so-called Western European group. The flared and beveled muzzle, however, does not conform to this group and mimics English style, a mimicry

that continues in the profile and diamond cross section of the buttstock, although the entire stock decoration is overwhelmingly French.

One of the salient characteristics of better quality French stocks of the early seventeenth century is the consistent use of combined brass and silver wire and engraved mother-of-pearl plaques. Brass wire is inlaid in borders and volutes in the normal manner, but more significantly is drawn into wire of decorative cross section that is cut into short lengths and is nailed into the stock. Seen here as tiny six-pointed stars, it more commonly appears elsewhere as dots and ovoid leaves (see No. 2). On these stocks a standard vocabulary of design elements is executed in engraved mother-of-pearl, consisting principally of winged cherubic heads, draped classical heads, owls and other naturalistic birds, and insects, as well as more conventional designs. The stock inlay incorporates the entire spectrum of this vocabulary. The French wheel-lock pistol No. 1, while somewhat coarser in execution, displays the same inlay technique including the six-pointed stars. Numerous other related pieces that have the same stock

[2] Ibid., pl. 42, no. 2.

[15]

inlay characteristics are fitted with French wheel-locks.[3] One other strongly French detail is the rolled comb superimposed on the pseudo-English stock.

On the surface, this piece seems to conform to the 1622 date engraved on the lock, but as we have stated, inspection reveals a close affinity with French firearms of the 1630s. The incongruity between the severity of the English elements and the elaboration of the remainder of the arm results from a French attempt to manufacture an English firearm in its national style. Obviously the lock and triggerguard could have been decorated en suite, but in order to preserve their English identity, they were not. This practice of manufacturing arms in a foreign style is supported by other *Cabinet d'Armes* inventory references.[4]

Provenance: Sotheby (William G. Renwick Collection, Pt. I), July 17, 1972, lot 8.
Overall length, 51 in. (129.5 cm.); barrel, 36¼ in. (92 cm.); caliber, .58

---

[3] John Forrest Hayward, *European Firearms* (London: H. M. Stationery Office, 1955), p. 43, no. 21.

[4] No. 169, "Un beau mousquet maniere de Turquie."

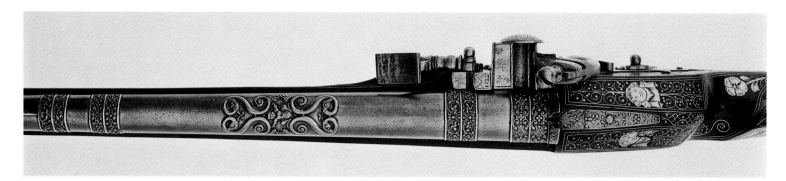

3

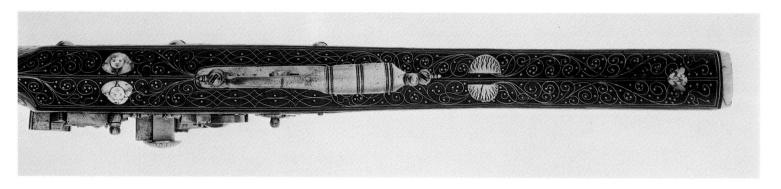

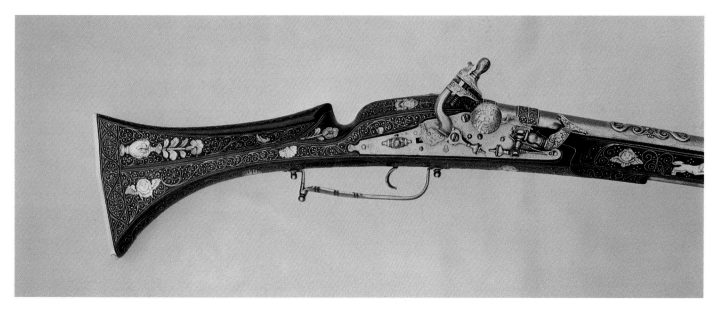

3

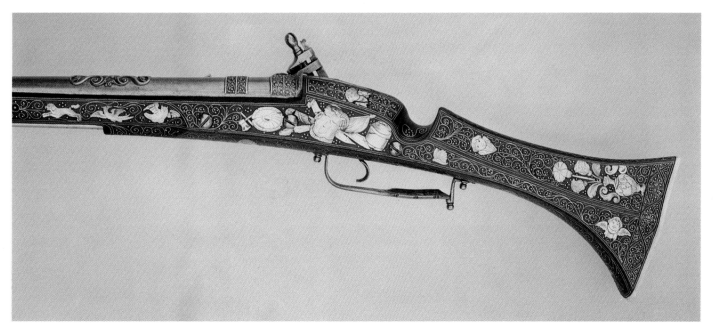

4 *Wheel-lock Pistol*

FRENCH, ca. 1640

THE fruitwood full stock is inlaid with silver wire to accentuate the facets; the eight-sided pommel terminates in an iron rosette. A full octagonal barrel tapers from the breech to a slightly expanded muzzle with the maker's mark, which appears to be DD in an oval, stamped into the upper breech. The lock, with engraved borders and rosette on the external wheel, has a pancover release button. An iron sideplate supports the wheel arbor and the piece is fitted with an iron triggerguard.

This pistol exhibits the simple elegance seen in many French arms of the first half of the seventeenth century. In this respect it is strongly associated with the Lisieux school, in which major emphasis is on the overall form. Here, silver wire inlay accentuates the linear form of the stock and serves to delineate its various planes.

Several features tend to contradict the earlier appearance of this pistol—the very slightly tapered octagonal barrel that lacks the moldings and extreme taper of earlier barrels, the thin profile of the dog neck, and the straight angular dog bridle. A pair of pistols by François du Clos in the Metropolitan Museum of Art, New York (04.3.192–193), display most of these lock features and have the barrel form characteristic of flintlock arms of ca. 1650, with a short sixteen-sided section separating the octagonal breech from the round forward portion. The forward end of the lockplate and its wood surround, the balustrate ramrod pipe, and the ovoid iron pommel are characteristics that accompany this style of barrel. Dr. Lenk has suggested that the du Clos pistols may form a garniture with the 1636 Musée de l'Armée gun, however, for the reasons given we must disagree. The basic form and style of these wheel-lock pistols was arrived at in France in the first decade of the seventeenth century and survived with only the slightest changes for the next fifty years.

Provenance: Sotheby (Runes Collection, Pt. I), June 11, 1964, lot 43.
Overall length, 23¾ in. (60.3 cm.); barrel, 16⅝ in. (42.2 cm.); caliber, .51

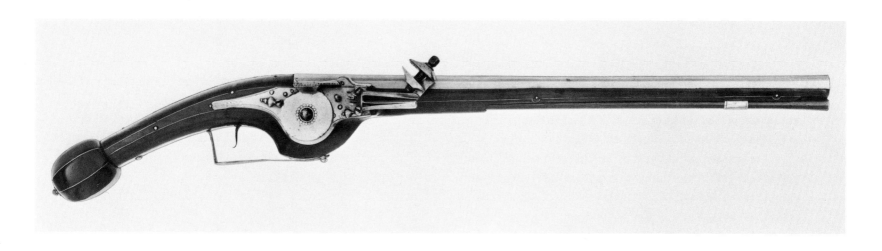

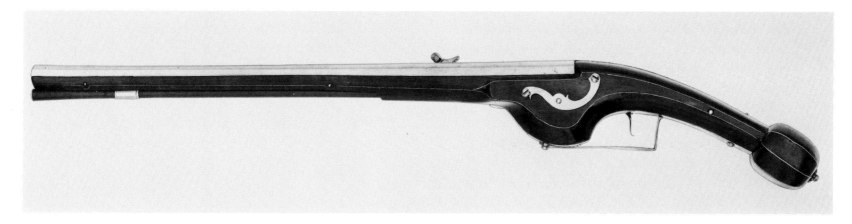

5 *Wheel-lock Pistol*

FRENCH (FIGEAC), ca. 1640

THE fruitwood full stock is relief carved with borders and foliage, and, between the lock and the ramrod entry, with military trophies in high relief. The grip is fitted with an engraved silver band followed by a laminated series of light and dark woods and ivory; it terminates in an ebony pommel carved as a grotesque human face with a floral surround. The plain barrel is in two stages: the breech is round with top and side flats that terminate at a weak molding; the remainder is round. The lock, of French type, has an external wheel and a heavily beveled plate. It is engraved, has light piercings, and ends in a chiseled and gilded human mask. The signature *A Figeac P[ar?] cisteron* is engraved on the upper bevel of the lockplate. The iron triggerguard is pierced, engraved, and gilded; the iron sideplate is engraved; the ramrod pipe is engraved gilt silver. The plain iron forend cap is attached to the barrel by a screw, and the iron ramrod tip has an engraved border.

Cisteron is known only by his signature, which appears on several pistols. A pair by him in the Wallace Collection (A1180 and 1181) are closely related to the one discussed here in their construction and decoration.

The date given this pistol is derived from three stylistic developments. The first and most conclusive is the design of the gilded mask on the tail of the lockplate, which indicates that Cisteron was inspired by pl. 3 of Philippe Cordier's patterns of 1635. The remainder of the lock engraving is also in the Cordier style. Second, the Wallace Collection pistols have carved animal head pommels relating to French flintlock arms of the 1640s. Also related to this flintlock group are the raised panels extending down the grip of this pistol from the lock, barrel tang, and sideplate.

The heavy stock carving forward of the lock may at first seem unusual, but it occurs on a few French arms of the 1630s and 1640s. Patterns for this type of carving appear in the later pattern books of Jean Bérain (1659) and Thuraine and le Hollandois (1660). By the time the patterns appeared in these publications, they were included only as survivals of an earlier style; therefore, carving of this type is seldom found on arms of the Thuraine and le Hollandois style.

Overall length, 27½ in. (69.8 cm.); barrel, 19⅜ in. (49.2 cm.); caliber, .58

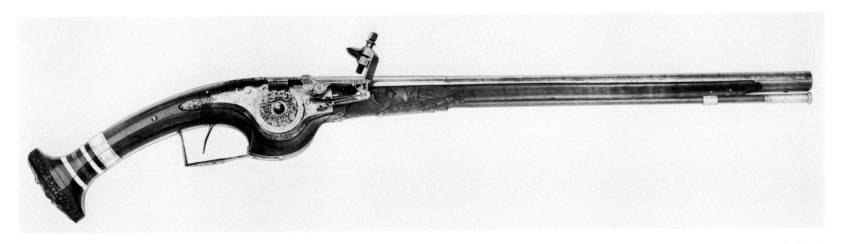

6 Flintlock Wender Pistol

FRENCH (LYONS), ca. 1650

THE two-piece stock is carved with borders and relief moldings; the forend is made of curly walnut, and the grip is of crotch walnut with round ebony inlays to the rear of the lockplate, tang molding, and sideplate. The tapered barrels have a full-length sighting bead and two flanking beads extending approximately one-third of the way to the muzzle. The barrel breech and forward segment of the swivel are engraved in floral designs. A flat, unbeveled lockplate is fully engraved with a bear hunt in an exotic setting. The cock is deeply engraved and is pierced with volutes. The maker's name, C[*laude*] *Cunet A Lyon*, appears on the head of the cock retaining bolt. Two forward lock sections supporting the pan and battery are also engraved. A projecting hook just forward of the triggerguard keeps the lower battery closed when the piece is primed. A pierced and engraved steel sideplate represents a grotesque dragonlike monster. There is a simple iron triggerguard that also serves to release the swivel mechanism. The buttcap has an engraved border of reel and bead and acanthus leaves. It terminates in a relief-chiseled flower and a turned button. The numeral 1 is stamped in the stock behind the tang and to the rear of the sideplate.

The wender rotating over-and-under action, with its reverse mounted mainspring and resulting elongated lockplate, provides an ideal surface for the engraver. The hunting scene depicted here gives a Germanic flavor to the lock, while the remainder of the engraving is in the style of designs later published by Francois Marcou. The unusual sideplate in the form of a bugle-nosed serpentine monster closely resembles a print, pulled from an engraved sideplate, now in the Victoria and Albert Museum (19057). Artistically, the most outstanding feature of this pistol is the superior quality of its lock engraving. The symmetrical forestock with a central cove molding on both sides and no provision for a ramrod is unusual. A similar pistol by Cunet in the Wrangel Armory, Skokloster, Sweden, is pictured in Lenk, *Flintlock*, pl. 26.

Provenance: Geoffrey Jenkinson, London, 1963.
Overall length, 25½ in. (64.7 cm.); barrel, 18½ in. (47 cm.); caliber, .51

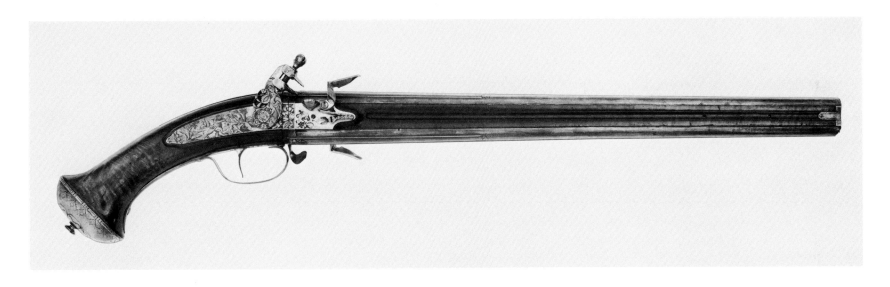

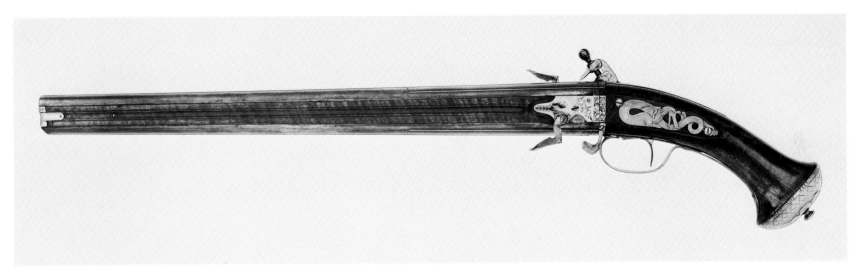

7 *Pair of Flintlock Wender Pistols*

FRENCH (TOUL), ca. 1650

THE maple stocks are inlaid with brass nails and silver wire foliate designs, some of which outline dark mastic inlays. Two parrots cut from sheet silver perch to the rear of the tang, flanking the raised molding. On the round barrels, sighting flats extend forward from the breech to within about three inches of the muzzle, showing that the barrels have been shortened to approximately two-thirds of their original length. The breech of each barrel is inlaid with delicate floral designs in copper and brass that compliment the engraving of the lock and swivel-breech sections. The lockplates, signed *Nicolas * Vincent a Toul* and *Vincent a Toul* respectively on the lower edge of their pan sections, terminate in gilt monster heads of applied bronze chased in low relief, while the cock bases are formed as coiling serpents around the gilded screw. Beneath each lock, just forward of the pierced and gilt iron triggerguard, is the turned latch that releases the swivel mechanism. The remaining mounts are of engraved gilt bronze and are partly pierced; the engraved gilt bronze butt-caps are highlighted with four silver panels and terminate in iron rosettes.

The decoration of these pistols is particularly interesting because it represents two design concepts that appear in published seventeenth-century pattern books. In the decoration of the stock inlay the artisan utilizes designs in the style of those published by Thomas Picquot in 1638. The design of other ornaments is of a type published by the gunsmith François Marcou in 1657. The pistols precede Marcou's designs, however, since these designs were already obsolete by the time of their publication, but were fashionable when these pistols were manufactured.

Provenance: Hôtel Drouot sale, Paris, December 5, 1966, lot 170. Overall length, 16¾ in. (42.5 cm.); barrel, 8⅞ in. (22.5 cm.); caliber, .56

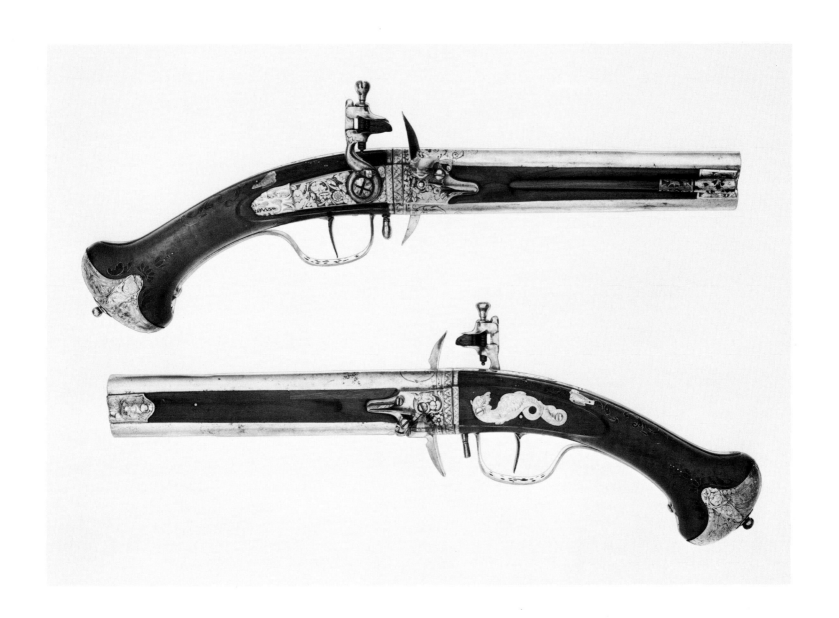

8 *Flintlock Pistol*

FRENCH (PARIS), ca. 1645

THE stock is curly walnut. The octagonal and round blued barrel has gold damascene decoration and is inscribed P. LAON A PARIS in gold along the top flat. The flat lockplate has a beveled edge and is engraved with a seated classical figure holding a shield upon which is engraved *Pierre Langon Paris*. Engraving fills the recessed area at the tail of the lock and the flat surface of the cock, which also has pierced volutes. The mounts consist of iron triggerguard, forend cap, ramrod tip, and a forward thimble, all of which are damascened against a black ground. A gilt bronze buttcap is chased in the form of an eagle's head backed by that of a lion, and has a grotesque human mask under the beak.

The full signature Pierre Langon engraved on the lockplate may be considered the gunsmith's true name, while the "Laon" on the barrel possibly results from the damascener's error. The only other example of an arm by Langon is a pistol in Lowenburg Castle (W1157), which appears to be the mate to the one illustrated here. It is shown in Lenk, *Flintlock*, pl. 21, where, in spite of the identical inconsistency between lock and barrel signatures, it can be seen that there are variances in the workmanship of the two pistols.

On this lock we again see an example of the decorative elements that were standard on Paris firearms used a decade before their first appearance in published form. These are the designs codified by Marcou in 1657. At the same time the damascene ornament imitates the lacy symmetrical foliate designs by Picquot popular since their publication in 1638. The buttcap is also closely related in concept to those pictured in Picquot. Particularly effective decoratively is the use of the damascening on the barrel at points where there is an abrupt change of form. This is one of the rare examples in which the quality of the engraving on the lock actually is as fine as that of the pattern books themselves. The combination of the slender lines and the excellence of the applied ornament achieves a unity of both quality and design.

Provenance: Jackson Arms, Dallas, Texas, 1970.
Overall length, 27½ in. (69.8 cm.); barrel, 20⅝ in. (52.3 cm.); caliber, .54

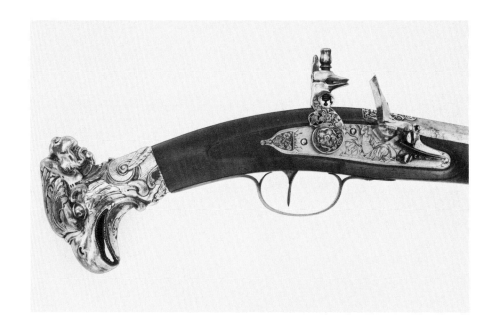

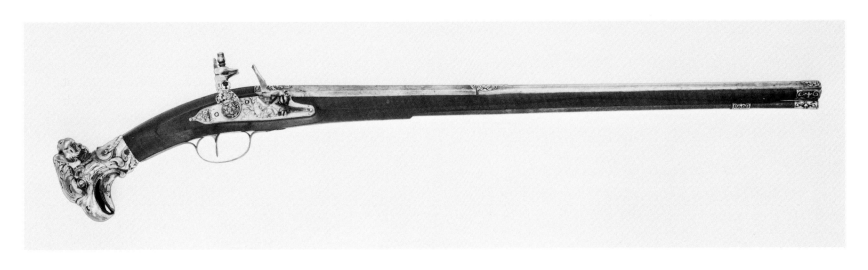

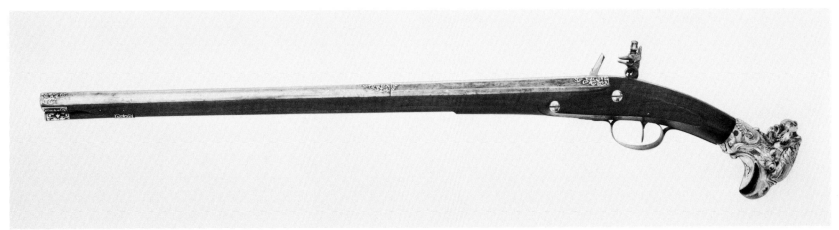

9 Pair of Flintlock Wender Pistols

FRENCH (?), ca. 1650

THE plain walnut stocks are in two pieces. The barrels are octagonal for about one-third of their length and have a turned molding at their transition to the round forward section. Punched decorations at the breech make a cursory attempt at a floral scroll, which is repeated on the swivel mechanism and the triggerguard. The latter is also coarsely engraved. The back-action lock has plain flat surfaces as do its two separate forward sections that contain the battery and pan and are attached to each of the rotating barrels. The grips terminate in a brass pommel in the form of an eagle's head backed by a human mask. The plain brass ramrod pipes are later replacements.

The form of the brass pommel is quite close to that of a signed pistol by Montagu of Metz that is illustrated in Lenk, *Flintlock*, pl. 28. Artistically, these pistols represent the more ordinary French production and stand in marked contrast to the preceding arms of approximately the same period, although the wender action was probably relatively costly in any form. Note that the barrels of both pistols are shown partially swiveled in the photograph.

Provenance: Leslie Scott, London.
Overall length, 25 in. (63.5 cm.); barrel, 18¾ in. (47.5 cm.); caliber, .43

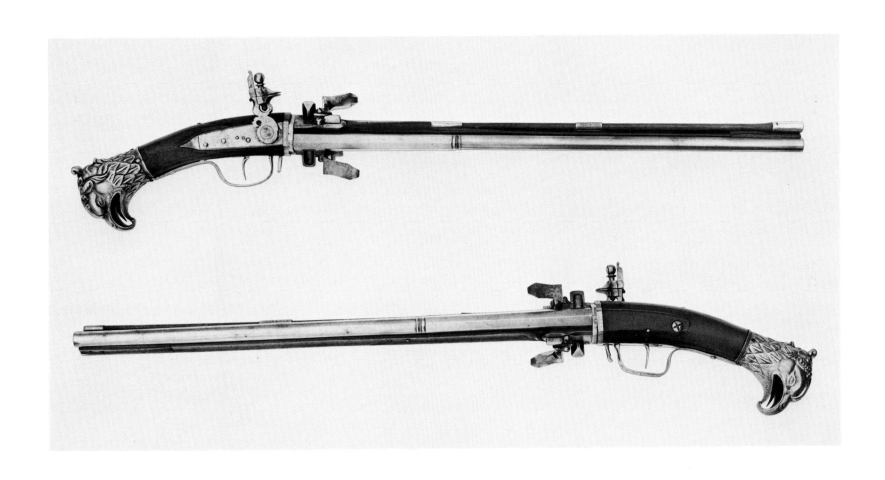

10 *Pair of Flintlock Rifled Cannon-Barrel Pistols*

FRENCH (PARIS), ca. 1665

THE stocks, of lightly curled walnut, have carved borders for all fittings. The barrels are rifled and formed in three stages: the octagonal barrel breech, blued with gold damascene designs, reduces to a plain short round section, which again steps down at a molded ring and tapers slightly to a reinforced ring-turned muzzle. The barrels unscrew for loading at the juncture of the octagonal and round sections. The locks form a unit with the barrel breech plug. Iron mounts are gold damascened, and a signature in gold script, *des Granges a Paris*, appears on the long barrel tangs.

The date assigned to these pistols is derived from their rounded triggerguard contours, which appear to be their latest feature. This form of guard was used by des Granges on the pair of pistols ordered by Erik Dahlberg in 1668 for the privy councillor to King Charles XI of Sweden, Svante Banér. Other elements—the serpentine of the cock that is more extended than in the 1668 examples, its attachment by a bolt rather than by a slotted screw, and the short-spurred pommel flattened in cross section—all relate to the late 1650s and early 1660s.

John Hayward has pointed out the possibility that two pistols of this same form that bear the signatures of the English makers Harman Barne and Truelocke may actually have originated in des Granges's Paris shop.[1] A further analysis of these pistols in comparison with English examples suggests that they may well be the prototypes of the English Queen Anne pistols of the eighteenth century.

Provenance: Scott & O'Shaughnessy, Inc., sale catalogue of rare antique guns and pistols, November 19–21, 1918, lot 229; Parke-Bernet, New York (Edward H. Litchfield), December 5, 1951, lot 49.
Overall length, 16½ in. (42 cm.); barrel, 11 in. (28 cm.); caliber, .50

---

[1] Hayward, *Gunmaker*, I, pp. 215–216, pl. 52c.

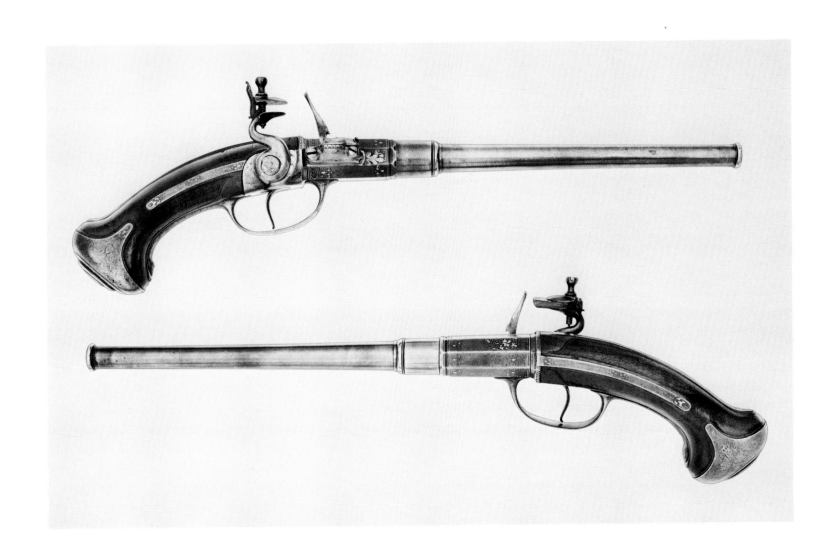

11 *Flintlock Pistol*

FRENCH (PARIS), ca. 1685

THE burl maple stock is relief carved with foliate designs and raised border moldings. The barrel is octagonal for a very short section of the breech and round for the remainder, with a raised sighting rib interrupted by chiseled ornament. The rib's rear portion is engraved THVRAINE; the forward, which extends to the front sight, A PARIS. Convex lock surfaces are relief chiseled, engraved, and signed THVRAINE Λ PARIS. The top jaw of the cock and its screw are later replacements. The serpentine iron sideplate is pierced and is chiseled in relief. The front extension of the iron trigger-guard is in the form of an urn and leaf finial. Two balustrate pipes hold the ramrod. A spurred iron pommel is nicely engraved with fantastic scenes and terminates in a grotesque mask, and there is a pierced and chased silver escutcheon.

Thuraine and le Hollandois, gunsmiths to Louis XIV, are best known for their authorship of a design book whose exact date is unknown, although some issues are dated 1660. The duration of their partnership is obscure, but they must have been working throughout most of the 1650s because the impressive group of designs in their book appears to represent a fairly large production that spanned a number of years. In spite of this, only two guns and a pair of pistols[1] with their joint signatures are known.

This partnership was apparently dissolved during the 1660s; a gun in the Tøjhusmuseum, Copenhagen, is signed with the single signature THVRAINE A PARIS and has the owner's name CORFITZ-TROLLE 1669 engraved on the barrel. Le Hollandois also appears to have remained in Paris. Both masters had sons who followed them in the trade there.

This pistol is probably the work of only the elder Thuraine, since a garniture of a fowling piece and two pairs of pistols in the Tøjhusmuseum, also dating from this period, are signed in the plural LES THVRAINES A PARIS.[2] The elegance of the Louis XIV classical style is exemplified by the pistol illustrated. Its form and most of its decorative elements belong to the 1680s and are documented by dated arms as well as by Simonin's first design book (1685). However, designs reminiscent of the earlier Thuraine and le Hollandois fashion are engraved on both sides of the pommel and between the cock and the pan. In conjunction with the Louis XIV style, these elements combine in a successful and effective blending of ornamentation that spans a quarter-century.

Provenance: Charles H. Moses, Ashtabula, Ohio, 1966.
Overall length, 20½ in. (52 cm.); barrel, 14 in. (36 cm.); caliber, .62

---

[1] Stephen V. Grancsay, ed., *Master French Gunsmiths' Designs of the XVII–XIX Centuries, Reproduced in Facsimile* (New York: Winchester Press, 1970), p. 12.

[2] Hayward, *Gunmaker*, I, p. 156.

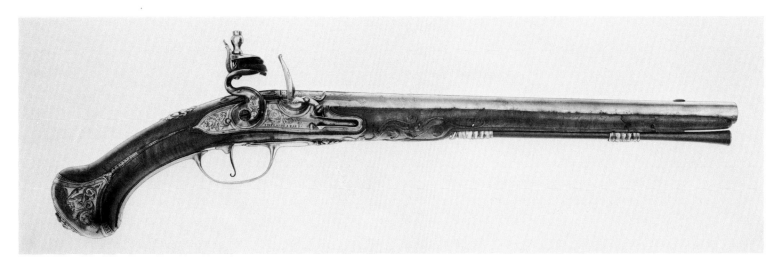

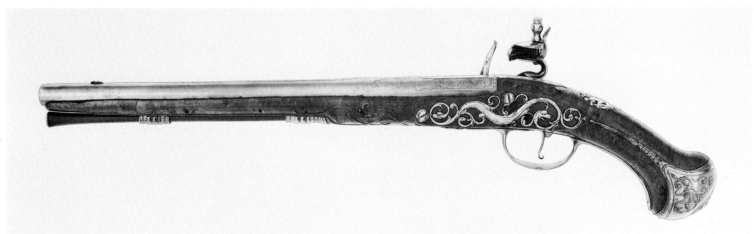

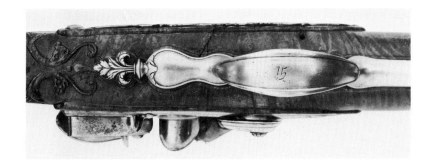

12 *Pair of Flintlock Pistols*

FRENCH (PARIS), dated 1697

STOCKS of fine quality burled walnut stump, carved with foliate designs incorporating animal heads and molded borders, are inlaid with silver wire. The barrels are round with raised sighting ribs engraved PIRAVBE·AVX·GAL-LERIES·A·PARIS·1697. The raised ring molding at the breech is interrupted by two side flats formed in two stages. Engraving that extends from the breech molding to the sighting rib frames relief-chiseled classical motifs. The muzzle is lightly engraved between the sighting rib and the front sight. The flat-surface locks are engraved with the same inscription as the barrels in addition to floral designs, borders, and a trophy of arms. The battery is chiseled in relief; the iron mounts are both engraved and chiseled.

Bertrand Piraube was unquestionably the most important figure in the decorative development of French firearms during the Louis XIV classical period, and by extension in European firearms as a whole. In 1670 he received *logement* in the *Galeries du Louvre*, and from that date until about 1710 his arms established the standard for European quality and design. Unlike his contemporaries, Piraube dated the majority of his arms. These two factors have enabled Dr. Torsten Lenk to trace the evolution of Parisian firearms during their most influential period.

These pistols are the second known example of the new "Bérain" style, which was in reality a reintroduction of mid-seventeenth-century design elements modified and combined with entirely new features. The first examples of this style, also a pair by Piraube, are dated 1696, just one year earlier than these pistols; they are discussed and illustrated by Lenk.[1] On the 1696 pistols, however, only two elements of the "Bérain" style are present—the flat lock surfaces and the faceted ramrod pipes. Piraube had not yet abandoned the full-length openwork sideplate or other elements of classical Louis XIV design. On this pair, however, all the elements have progressed into the new fashion. The shorter sideplate with the uniting oval medallion and its vestigial tail formed by silver wire, as well as the engraved oval medallions on either side of the pommels, are modified revivals of designs published by Thuraine and le Hollandois ca. 1660. The inset geometrical panels of the triggerguards, however, are entirely new. Panels of this same design as well as other elements of the new style were first published in the de la Collombe supplement to the 1705 reissue of Simonin's book. The example of these pistols affords an excellent insight into the evolution of Parisian pattern books of the seventeenth and eighteenth centuries. Typical of the Paris trade at this period, styles were well established by working gunsmiths long before they were published.

Provenance: Charles H. Moses, Ashtabula, Ohio, 1966.
Overall length, 21¾ in. (55.3 cm.); barrel, 15⅛ in. (38.3 cm.); caliber, .61

---

[1] *Flintlock*, p. 110, pl. 85.

[34]

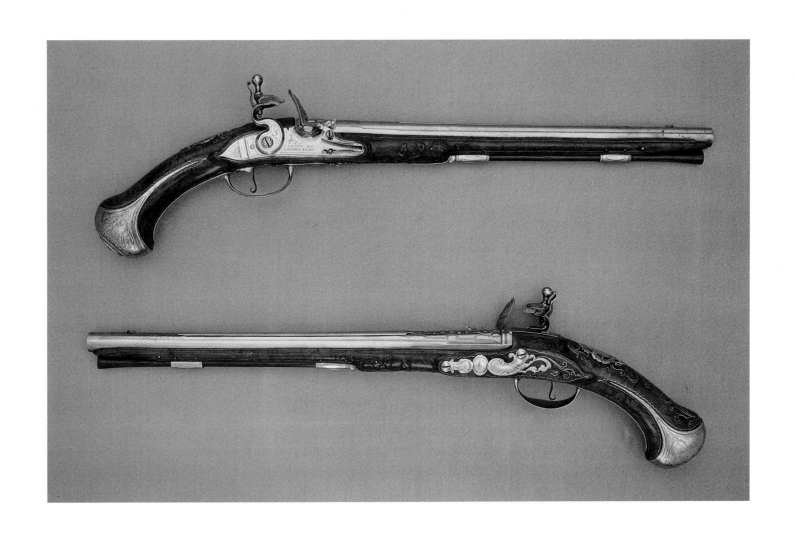

12

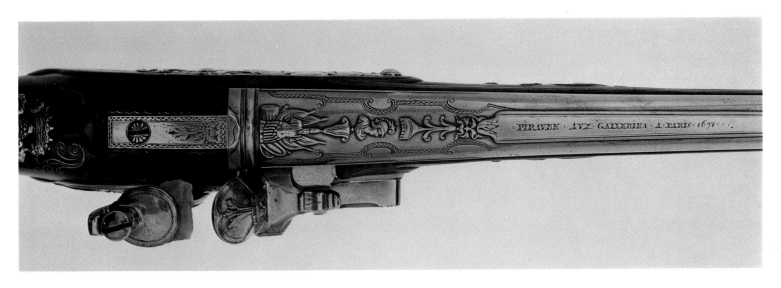

12

13 *Flintlock Wender Gun*

FRENCH (PARIS), ca. 1705

THE two-piece stock of stump walnut has relief-carved borders and foliage. The browned barrels have octagonal breeches for one-fifth of their length and become round for the remainder. A sighting flat continues nearly to the muzzle, where it is fitted with an elongated silver sight. The breeches are lightly engraved with borders and have the intertwined initials *JS*(?) on the top facet. The lock has flat surfaces engraved with borders, trophies, and foliate scrolls. The lockplate has the engraved inscription *Languedoc A Paris*. The swivel mechanism is engraved with borders, and its latch release is the forward extension of the triggerguard. The triggerguard bow acts as the spring of the mechanism. A thin brass friction washer separates the two iron plates of the swivel. The engraved iron mountings are chiseled. The top

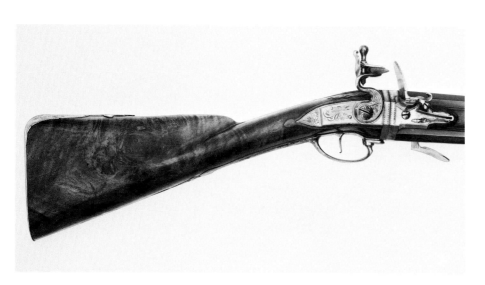

extension of the buttplate has the engraved date 1724. A chiseled iron plaque with a threaded hole is inlaid in the lower buttstock between the triggerguard finial and the buttplate. The horn-tipped baleen ramrod is held by three diamond-faceted ramrod pipes.

Laurent le Languedoc is first documented in the 1685 pattern book of Claude Simonin, the title plate of which states that he was "Gunsmith Of The King" and that the designs included were taken from his works. He dated many of his arms; the latest recorded date is 1722. Considering his extreme importance in the transmission of French firearms design, Languedoc has been insufficiently dealt with by arms historians. Not only did his arms provide the Louis XIV classical style designs in Simonin's pattern book, but in 1705 he personally reissued the original Simonin book with supplemental plates illustrating the new "Bérain" style. These two editions formally define for the first time the fashions that dominated European firearms design for more than a century. They circulated throughout Europe and were extremely influential in disseminating Languedoc's interpretation of the styles. While other Paris masters were largely responsible for their development and limited distribution in the case of arms made for foreign courts, it was Languedoc's published patterns, used by hundreds of gunsmiths in the cities and towns of Western Europe, that heightened internationally the artistic standard of flintlock arms. Numerous arms in the Bedford Collection have been strongly influenced, directly or indirectly, by one or the other of these publications.

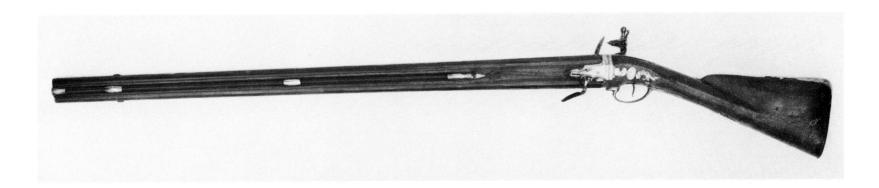

Not only has Languedoc's influence been neglected, so has the extensive production of his shop. Compared to the existing output of many of his best known Paris contemporaries, a surprising number of his arms still survive—twenty-two in Dresden alone—although a recent book on that collection does not mention even one.

This gun and the Languedoc pistols in No. 14 are multiple-shot firearms. Interestingly, two of the seven arms plates in the 1685 pattern book, and two more of the four in his 1705 supplement, are devoted to the wender and fixed over-and-under systems.

In 1962 this gun and the following pistols were sold at Sotheby's (November 30, lot 109), where they were listed as a garniture. However, there are enough significant differences in workmanship and decoration to raise serious doubts as to whether they began life together. In fact, the pistols seem to date a good decade later than the gun. Moreover, the barrel monograms, while very similar, do not appear to be identical, although this may indicate only that they were executed at a different time and by a different hand, and might be the result of separate purchases by the same individual. It certainly appears that these arms have been together since the final years of the eighteenth century, since they correspond to the description of a gun and pistols in

the collection of William Constable of Burton Constable, Yorkshire (1721–1791).[1]

The 1724 date on the extension of the buttplate has previously been accepted as representing the date of the gun. But a careful comparison with Languedoc arms reveals that the form of the buttstock is related to arms that he produced from 1700 to 1710. In this example the lower profile of the stock is virtually straight, and the straight profile of the comb is nearly parallel to the barrels. By 1715 to 1720 a form of buttstock had evolved in which both of these lines were curved, the lower edge being concave and the comb convex. The date does not appear to be a modern addition and may have been added at that time by a previous owner. Its engraving is inferior to that of the rest of the gun. Also, fire bluing was the customary barrel finish at the time this gun was made; the present brown finish dates no earlier than the mid-eighteenth century when it became the fashion and thus is a result of a later modernization.

Overall length, 51½ in. (130.8 cm.); barrel, 36⅝ in. (93 cm.); caliber, .62

---

[1] W. Keith Neal and D. H. L. Back, *Great British Gunmakers, 1740–1790: The History of John Twigg and the Packington Guns* (London: Sotheby Parke Bernet Productions, 1975), p. 94.

14 *Pair of Double-Barreled Flintlock Pistols*

FRENCH (PARIS), ca. 1715

THE matched crotch grain stocks are in two pieces and have raised borders. The browned over-and-under barrels are octagonal for the breech third, then gradually become round for their remainder. The breeches are engraved with panels. On the upper barrels are engraved the interlaced initials *JL*, and they have an elongated silver foresight. The flat-surfaced locks are engraved with borders, foliage, and military trophies. The right-hand lock of each pistol is signed LANGVE-DOC, the left, ·A· PARÍS. The iron triggerguards and ramrod pipes are faceted and lightly engraved. The iron pommels are engraved and terminate in a chiseled girdle and engrailed chiseled mask. The silver escutcheons are pierced and chased. The baleen ramrods have a horn tip.

These pistols differ from the preceding gun (No. 13) in that the barrels are fixed instead of rotating. This construction requires that each pistol have separate right- and left-hand locks. The system had been in use for more than a century and a half when these were made, and is also the subject of two plates in Simonin's 1685 pattern book that were taken from Languedoc's arms. The earliest flintlocks of this system have lockplates whose lower profiles are more or less straight. By 1660 the offset profile seen here was developed, thus slenderizing the stock from the barrels rearward. The extremely slender grip of these pistols, which produces the exaggerated flair of the pommels, indicates a date well into the first quarter of the eighteenth century. The barrels were apparently browned en suite with the preceding gun.

Overall length, 17½ in. (44.5 cm.); barrels, 11¼ in. (28.5 cm.); caliber, .68

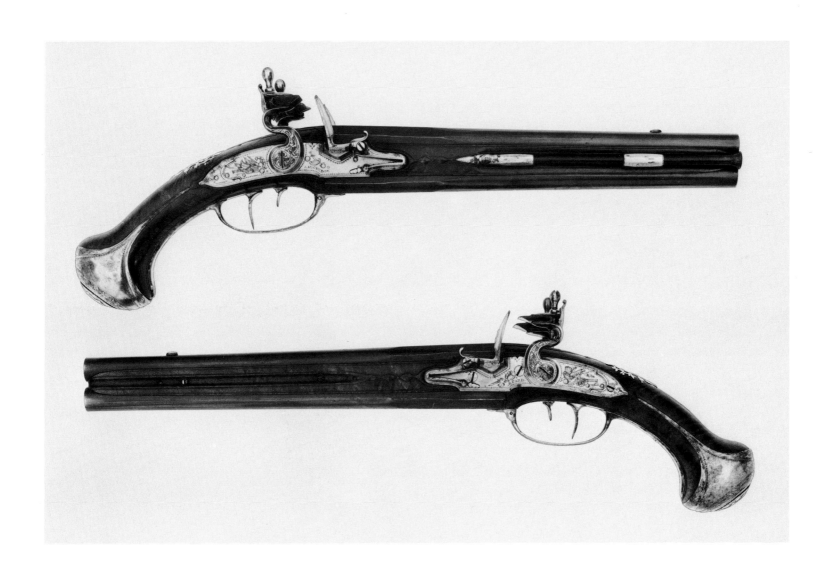

15 *Pair of Flintlock Pistols*

FRENCH (PARIS), ca. 1720

THE walnut stocks have carved borders and foliage. The barrels are octagonal at the breech, then become sixteen-sided. A turned and chiseled transitional band separates the breech from the round forward section. The muzzle is reinforced by a similarly decorated band. The breech facets are inlaid with gold wire, and the gold-lined mark and counter-mark of Diego Ventura are struck into the upper facet under three gold-lined fleurs-de-lis. The flintlocks with flat surfaces have engraved borders, foliage, and military trophies. The engraved signature DE ROY is in a riband over A PARIS under the pan. The cock has chiseled decoration over a damascened ground. The mounts are of chased and engraved silver; the sideplate and escutcheon are also pierced. The pommel bosses are decorated with portrait busts, one of a man, the other, of a woman in contemporary costume.

There is no known reference to the Paris gunsmith de Roy. However, Diego Ventura, who supplied the barrels, was a prominent Madrid gunsmith for more than fifty years. He lived to "a very advanced age" and was appointed gunsmith to Carlos III of Spain only two years before his death in 1762.

With the exception of the barrels, these pistols adhere precisely to a design formula in vogue during the first decade of the reign of Louis XV—the fully developed "Bérain" style. During this period silver mounts increased in popularity. Silver mounts, which were easily cast and chased, were a cheaper alternative to chiseled steel and represent a decline in overall quality standards. Although de Roy remains un-

identified, a clue to his Paris background may be found in an almost identically designed escutcheon on a pair of pistols made in 1696 for King Charles XI of Sweden by Charles Doucin of Paris. The ornament of the Doucin pistols was designed by Jean Bérain.[1] The gold wire barrel inlay is of inferior quality in design and execution when compared to that on other barrels by Ventura and to Paris work of the period. The obvious conclusion is that it was added at a date later than that of the pistols' manufacture.

Provenance: Joe Kindig, Jr., York, Pennsylvania, 1964.
Overall length, 18½ in. (47 cm.); barrel, 12¼ in. (31 cm.); caliber, .65

---

[1] Hayward, *Gunmaker*, II, pp. 39–41, pl. 4e.

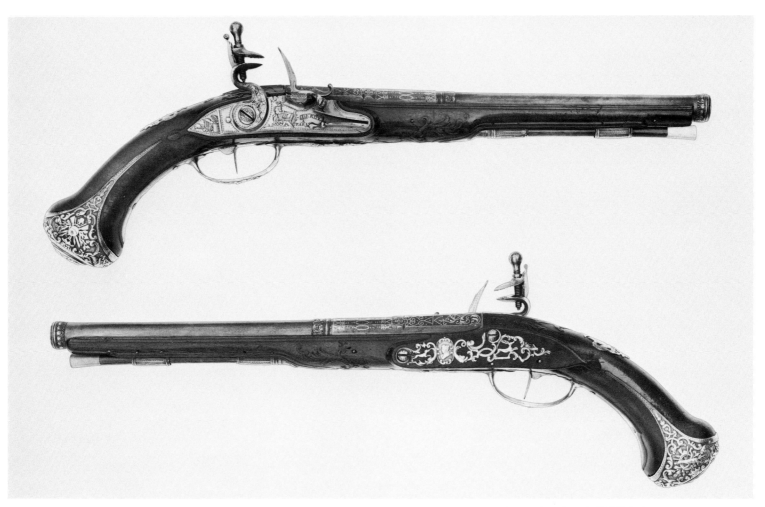

16 *Pair of Flintlock Pistols*

FRENCH (PARIS), ca. 1750

THE curly walnut stocks with raised moldings have rococo carving around the tang. The barrels in four stages alternate octagonal and round from the breech. They have a turned gilded ring reinforcing the muzzle upon which is mounted an iron blade front sight (one sight is lacking). The blued breech is decorated with floral designs, shells, borders, and the cursive initials AF(J?). The barrel tangs are damascened in a diaper pattern. The barrels unscrew for loading just forward of the abbreviated stock, and the short octagonal section accommodates a spanner. A ring and lug attached to the left side of the breech prevent the barrels from being completely separated when the forward section is removed for loading. Locks with flat surfaces are engraved with rococo designs, borders, and the inscription *Frappier A Paris*. The silver mounts are chased in rocailles. Iron belthooks pivot from the pommel.

The maker Frappier was at least a generation removed from the gunsmith of the same name who worked in Paris and was in partnership with the Huguenot gunsmith Monlong in the 1670s. Dr. Hoff has suggested that the barrel monogram may represent A. F(rappier) le J(eune).

Triggerguard and pommel designs are heavily rococo and appear to be directly influenced by designs published by de Marteau in 1743 and 1749, as is the engraving of the lock. The sideplates, however, with their piercings and medallion, relate to de la Collombe's 1705 patterns, although incorporating some rococo chasing.

Provenance: Rene Johnson; Frank E. Bivens, Los Angeles, California; Geoffrey Jenkinson, London.
Overall length, 13¾ in. (35 cm.); barrel, 8 in. (20.3 cm.); caliber, .52

17 *Pair of Flintlock Pistols*

FRENCH (PARIS), silver marks for 1789

THE abbreviated stump walnut stocks have carved moldings and rococo foliage around the barrel tang. The blued barrels are in three stages: a round breech section with side flats and a concave rear sight, a short octagonal section for spanning, and the remainder round with a reinforced muzzle. The breech and tang have damascened borders, trophies of arms, and the inscription SIMON ARQUEBU^{er} DU ROI A PARIS. The oval marks of Nicolas LeClerc flank the sight.[1] The lock surfaces are convex with raised borders and are inscribed SIMON ARQUEBUSIER DU ROY BREVETÉ DE MGR COMTE DARTOIS A PARIS. The silver mounts, chased in relief with rocailles and trophies, are struck with the charge mark, discharge mark, and warden's mark for the year beginning September 11, 1789.

The convex lock surfaces with raised rim borders and the relief-chiseled "bombs" on the battery show a revival of the fashion of the 1680s. The form of the pan with its bridle and the straighter profile of the lockplate, however, are obvious indicators of the pistols' true period. This is consistent with the heavy rococo decoration of the mounts. Simon's inscription, in which he calls himself gunsmith to the king, declares that he received his patent from Charles Philippe, Count of Artois, brother of Louis XVI, who later became Charles X of France.

Provenance: Hôtel Drouot sale, Paris, December 5, 1966, lot 180. Overall length, 15⅞ in. (40.3 cm.); barrel, 10⅛ in. (25.6 cm.); caliber, .58

---

[1] Lenk, *Flintlock*, pp. 115–116.

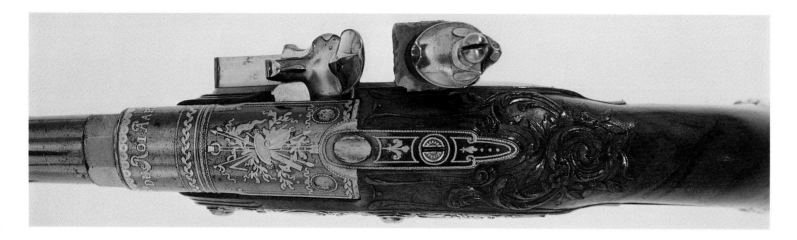

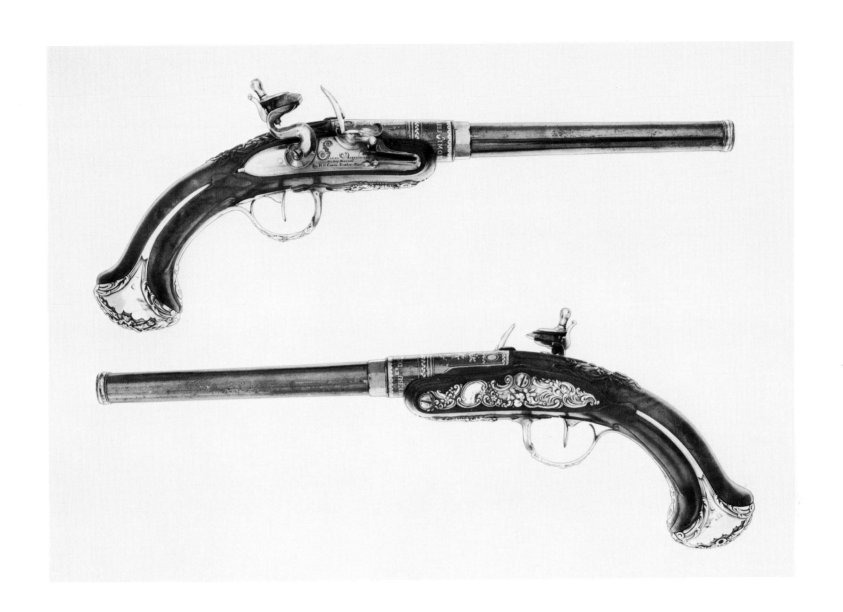

18 *Flintlock Pistol*

FRENCH (PARIS), ca. 1810

THE walnut stock, with a checkered grip, is heavily inlaid with engraved gold and silver plaques and engraved gold and silver wire. The full tapering octagonal rifled barrel flares slightly toward the muzzle. It is fitted with a false breech that has a rear sight and is gold damascened to contrast with a blackened ground. The inscription PENIET A PARIS is inlaid in gold. The flat surfaces of the lock are engraved, and the plate carries the same inscription as the barrel. There is a single set trigger. The silver mounts, which bear the Paris or provincial marks in use from June 19, 1798, to August 31, 1809, are chased and heavily engraved. The maker's mark, a diamond containing the initials DT flanking a caduceus, is also struck in the rear extension of the triggerguard. Directly below this is an unnumbered medium excise mark. The triggerguard finial has an inset of a classical warrior's head in gilt copper. The ramrod is ivory tipped.

This pistol typifies the Napoleonic Empire style, which superimposes on a new form a potpourri of two hundred years of French gunmaking design. The right-angled grip and flattened pommel represent a radical departure from pre-revolutionary style, while the silver inlay composed of engraved sheet and wire revives a seventeenth-century concept. Surprisingly, not only the general concept, but specifically the grotesque mask engraved on the rear thimble, shows that the engraver knew pl. 6 of Simonin's 1685 design book. Likewise, classical elements, baroque swags, and ribbons are all inherited from the seventeenth century. Although the form of the triggerguard and the cock originated in the mideighteenth century, the heavy rococo style of the immediate past is rejected. The approach, however, with its profusion of design, appears to be an attempt to continue the rococo concept while eliminating its specific elements.

Provenance: Sumner Healey, New York City.

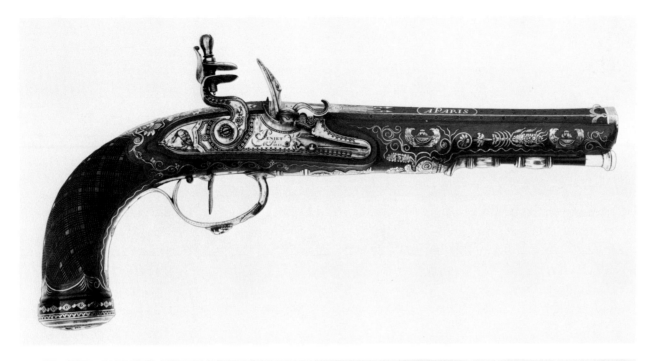

19 *Cased Pair of Flintlock Pistols*

FRENCH (VERSAILLES), ca. 1818

THE curly walnut full stocks have relief-carved borders, foliage, and scales. The multigrooved rifled barrels are fully octagonal, engraved, gilded, and blued. They are stamped at the breech with three identical marks—BOUTET within an extended octogan (Støckel 102)—and have silver bead front sights. Their blue gray case-hardened locks, with flat surfaces and relief gold inlay depicting a wolf and dragon, have rainproof pans and friction rollers on the battery springs. One is signed in gold on the lower bevel N.N. BOUTET A VERSAILLES, the other, MANUFACTURE ROYALE A VERSAILLES. The triggers are single-set with an adjustment screw in their back plates. The chased silver mounts are parcel gilt except for the plain gold escutcheon engraved *Bolivar* in script. The sideplate depicts the battle of the Centaurs and Lapiths against a mat ground; the triggerguard, classical trophies and a female half-figure; the extension of the rear pipe, a Medusa's head; and the buttcap, a helmeted classical mask. The baleen ramrods have a silver tip. All mounts except the ramrod tips and forward thimbles are stamped with the fasces provincial restricted warranty mark for the period September 1, 1809, to August 15, 1819. In addition, the sideplate, buttcap, and inner surface of the triggerguard bow have the circular helmeted head provincial medium excise mark for the same period. The number 94 on the helmet indicates the Versailles Bureau of Control. Also in the triggerguard bow are the provincial first standard silver mark and the maker's mark of Nicolas Boutet. The latter shows a pocket pistol between the letters N.B. contained within a vertical diamond frame.

The silver-trimmed rosewood case is lined with green velvet, and inside the lid a gold-tooled red leather lining bears the legend MANUFACTURE ROYALE A VERSAILLES 1825. N.N. BOUTET. LE DEPÒT DE LA MANUF^RE A PARIS, RUE DES FILLES ST. THOMAS NO. 23. An oval silver plaque inlaid in the outside of the lid is engraved N.N. BOUTET À VERSAILLES. The green velvet interior is fitted for the pistols and their accessories, which consist of a case-hardened bullet mold with its handle terminating in a wrench for the hooked barrel breech plugs; a tortoiseshell powder flask with silver gilt fittings; a T-handled steel cleaning rod; two brass-tipped rosewood loading rods, one fitted with a powder measure; a rosewood-handled hammer and a rosewood mallet; an octagonal iron oil can; a ball puller; a touch-hole pick; and a rosewood-handled screwdriver that is a modern replacement. There are two foil-lined covered compartments, one of which holds two cleaning jags. There are two keys to the case.

Nicolas Noël Boutet was born on August 31, 1761, the son of Noël Boutet, gunsmith to the king's light horse. In 1788 he married the daughter of a gunsmith in ordinary to the king, and by the terms of the marriage contract succeeded his father-in-law in that post. He worked at Versailles from 1788 to 1818, surviving the changes of government that followed the revolution.

A factory for the manufacture of military arms was established at Versailles in 1792, and in the following year Boutet was appointed its director under a twenty-five-year contract. In 1794 a special workshop to produce luxury arms was estab-

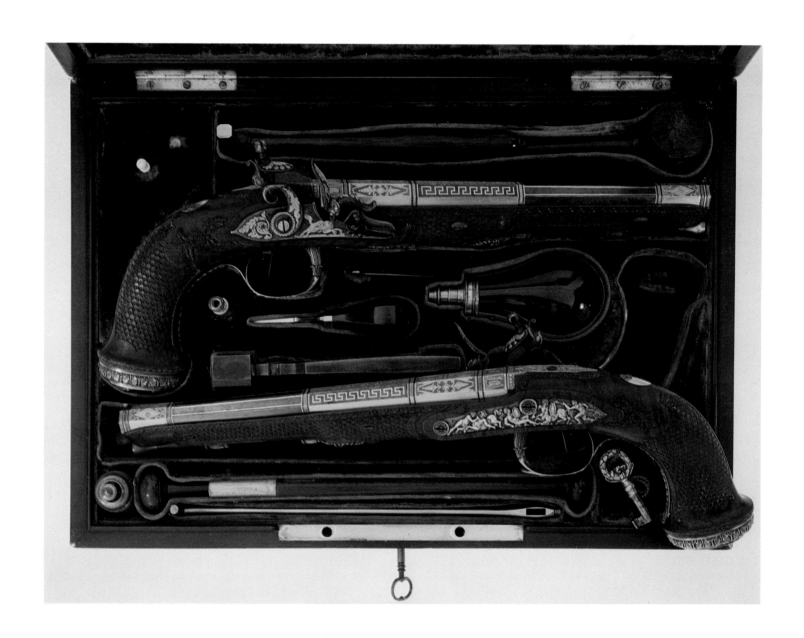

19

lished under Boutet's exclusive direction. On the expiration of his concession in 1818, he moved his shop to Paris, where he died in 1833.[1] Artistically, Nicolas Boutet was without a doubt the most important gunsmith of the nineteenth century.

The inscription *Bolivar* on the escutcheons is documented as referring to Simón Bolívar, Liberator of Venezuela. A notarized affidavit dated July 7, 1851, accompanying a bill of sale for these pistols from Enrique París to Enrique (Henry) Grice states that they were presented to Bolívar by the Marquis de Lafayette in 1825. It further notes that Bolívar subsequently gave the pistols to his close friend, José Ignacio París, father of the seller, and that Grice received them in the same condition as when they left the possession of Bolívar.[2]

Lafayette's visit to the United States in 1824–1825 probably had a direct bearing on the presentation of these pistols, since in that year members of Washington's family requested that he send a portrait of the late president to Simón Bolívar. A letter from Bolívar acknowledges the receipt of the portrait, but makes no reference to the pistols, which must have been Lafayette's personal gift.

These pistols were obviously made during the period between 1815 and 1818, that is, between the restoration of the monarchy and the expiration of Boutet's contract at the Versailles Manufactory. The inscription MANUFACTURE ROYALE was used after the accession of Louis XVIII in 1815. Furthermore, the silver marks coincide with this time period. Since the date 1825 and the address of the Paris depot of the Versailles Manufactory are stamped on the leather lining of the lid of the case, one can only conclude that during seven or more years these pistols and their case remained in storage. The leather label and the Bolívar inscription were

---

[1] Hayward, *Gunmaker*, II, pp. 189–191.
[2] Daniel A. del Río, "Pistols of the Liberator," *Quarterly Bulletin of the Bolivarian Society of the United States* (September 1973).

added at the time of presentation. The absence of a presentation inscription is curious, especially since the 1851 document states that they were presented by Lafayette in 1825. However, since Lafayette did not depart for France until early September of that year, the pistols may well have been ordered from America.

Provenance: Sotheby, March 19, 1973, lot 21.
Overall length, 16¼ in. (41.5 cm.); barrel, 10½ in. (26.7 cm.); caliber, .60
Case, 17¾ in. (45 cm.) x 12¼ in. (31 cm.)

20 Double-Barreled Tube Lock Gun

FRENCH (?), ca. 1820

THE stump walnut half-stock is checkered and studded at the grip and on the forend. The buttstock is unusual in having cheekpieces on both sides, which are overlaid with heavy cast and chased German silver dolphins and dogs; a similarly executed grotesque animal head terminates the grip. The stock has other overlays of lesser relief. The barrels are in two stages: the breech is octagonal with raised beading and is fully gilded to the transitional ring moldings; the blued round forward section terminates in a short gilded segment. The tang of the hooked breech is blued and holds the integral rear sight; a full-length gilded central rib is fitted with a gilded iron bead foresight. The original tube locks have case-hardening colors. Engraved with borders, the plate has an external safety behind the hammers, which are chiseled in the form of dolphins. A horizontally pivoting lever retains the tube primer. Mounts are of cast silver chased in high relief with classical masks and floral designs. The triggerguard grip rail and the top extension of the buttplate are marked with their maker's name, BROTBECK, and 13 in a circle.

The maker of this gun is unknown, but in style and workmanship it is very close to arms by Gauvin of Langres, France. The dolphins and grotesque head adorning the stock are so identical that they may have come from the same casting patterns as the decoration on the stock of a signed Gauvin double gun. The boldness of the interpretation of the Napoleonic style on both this and the Gauvin gun suggests a Germanic origin. This conclusion appears to be supported on the illustrated example by the Germanic name of the sil-versmith and by a mark associated with the Austro-Hungarian Empire.

The method used to produce the reliefs on the buttplate and triggerguard of this arm was occasionally employed on Napoleonic or Empire style firearms. The body of the mount and its relief elements were cast separately and then were joined by soldering. In this instance the body metal is of lower quality than that of its applied reliefs.

Provenance: W. Keith Neal, Warminster, England, 1963.
Overall length, 45¾ in. (116.2 cm.); barrel, 30 in. (76.1 cm.); caliber, .60

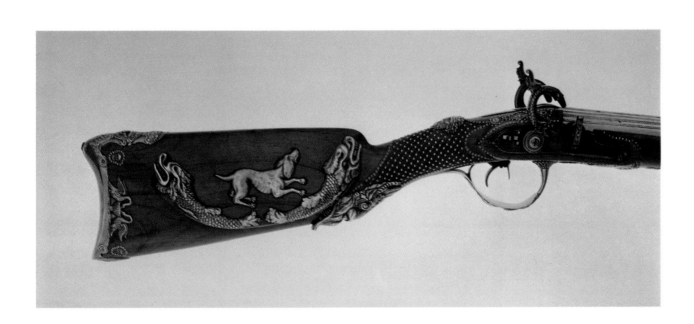

21 *Pair of Flintlock Pistols*

FRENCH (PARIS), ca. 1825

THE burl birch half-stocks are plain. Round twist barrels, originally blued, have a short octagonal breech section that is gold inlaid and is stamped with three oval marks: on the top flat, crossed fronds between the initials L.C.,[1] flanked by I.L.C. on the adjacent side flats. These are the marks of the Paris barrelmaker Jean LeClerc, who was probably related to Nicolas LeClerc (see No. 17). The touchhole is platinum lined. On the upper breech forward of the maker's marks are inlaid gold Arabic characters in an oval. The locks with flat surfaces retain their case-hardened colors and are engraved and lightly gold inlaid. They have platinum-lined rainproof pans and concealed battery springs. The same Arabic characters that are on the breech appear on the forward extension of the lockplate. Silver gilt mounts are decorated with pseudo-Turkish military trophies in relief. They have the restricted warranty mark for Paris silver for August 16, 1819, to May 9, 1838, and the maker's mark, LD in a diamond. The relief decoration of the mounts consists of repeated cast relief elements applied by silver soldering. Ramrods, tipped in silver gilt, have brass and iron worms.

While it is generally considered that "Turkish" pistols of this type were made for the Eastern trade or for presentation, they were also fashionable in England and on the Continent at this time (see No. 40).

Provenance: Geoffrey Jenkinson, London, 1969.
Overall length, 15 in. (38 cm.); barrel, 10 in. (25.5 cm.); caliber, .66

---

[1] Schedelmann, *Die grossen Büchsenmacher*, p. 269.

22 *Cased Pair of Percussion Pistols*

FRENCH (PARIS), ca. 1838

THE half-stocks are ebony with relief-carved borders and foliage. They are inlaid with engraved red gold foliage and an oval escutcheon engraved with the crowned monogram of King Victor Emmanuel II of Sardinia. The full octagonal barrels with multigroove rifling have a blued mat surface with chased gold overlay. The extreme breech has an iron bar sight, while the blade foresight is of red gold. The red gold percussion bolster spirals to form a flash guard. A polished blued and gold-framed section of the upper flat contains the gold-inlaid inscription PRELAT A PARIS. The flat-surfaced locks have applied gold plaques chased and engraved with classical motifs. The rear section of both lockplates has a mourning female figure; the forward section of the plate illustrated bears a dying warrior, the other, a dying Amazon. A winged dragon is on both hammer plaques, and the thumbpiece and hood of polished steel are shaped like a lion's head. The mounts are of gold with chased ornaments in Empire and classical themes: the fall of Phaeton appears on the sideplate, Hercules on one triggerguard, and warriors in combat on the other. The buttcaps are chased with an oak garland, one of which encloses the figure of Socrates, and the other, a statue of Jupiter. The ramrods end in chased gold tips.

All mounts except the forward ramrod pipe and ramrod tip are struck with Paris gold marks. The triggerguard spur is marked with the third standard mark for gold for the period August 16, 1819, to May 9, 1838. It also has the large excise mark for gold for the same period, and the restricted warranty mark for May 10, 1838, to the present. The lock-

plate, sideplate, cock, buttcap, and forend cap have restricted warranty marks for both the earlier and later periods mentioned above. The barrel tang and front extension of the triggerguard have only the restricted warranty mark for the earlier period.

The top and front of the ebony case are inlaid with engraved ormulu plaques in rococo revival designs. A central plaque is engraved with the crowned monogram of Victor Emmanuel II, king of Sardinia. The lining is blue velvet decorated with both plain and gold stampings. The interior is compartmented for the pistols and numerous accessories including a fluted iron powder flask with recessed panels containing damascened designs, its adjustable measure with chiseled bead borders, which is tipped with a fluted ivory finial, and a bullet mold, case hardened and damascened en suite with the flask. The ivory starting mallet is carved in baroque revival designs, as are the cap box, patch box, and loading and cleaning rods; the nipple wrench has an ivory handle carved en suite; and the octagonal oil can is of polished steel and has a gilt top with an acorn finial. There are two covered compartments for balls. A leather carrying case has its cover tooled in rococo revival designs.

François Prélat is best known for his early experiments and patents on fulminating powder and the percussion cap. He was established at 4 Rue des Trois Frères in Paris, and is known to have executed royal commissions for King Louis Philippe (see No. 23).

Gold-mounted firearms are extremely rare. In this instance the precise dating provided by the gold marks is an excep-

tional coincidence. The mounts had to be produced in 1838 when, at the time of the changeover in marks, a few were inadvertently double-struck.

The ornament of these pistols has departed little from the earlier Napoleonic Empire style. If anything, there is somewhat more emphasis on classical themes. Initially, these particular pistols are impressive because of the richness of their materials and the contrast of light and dark. Close inspection reveals the outstanding attention devoted to the most minute details.

Provenance: Jackson Arms, Catalogue 17, December 1960, Dallas, Texas.
Overall length, 15 in. (38.1 cm.); barrel, 9⅝ in. (24.3 cm.); caliber, .58

22

22

23 *Cased Pair of Percussion Pistols*

FRENCH (PARIS), dated 1845

THE stump walnut half-stocks are carved with scrolls and gothic panels and are inlaid with the ivory initials PS and two silver escutcheons around the barrel key entry. The rifled damascus barrels are fully octagonal and have a gold bead foresight. They are blued and have gold damascened borders and floral decoration. Each bears the inscription PRELAT A PARIS in damascened gothic letters, and their tangs are numbered 1 and 2 respectively. The percussion locks are decorated en suite with the barrels; on the pistol numbered 2, the lock is signed *Prelat*, and *A Paris* continues on pistol number 1. The iron mounts are blued and damascened en suite with the barrel and lock.

The walnut case is inlaid with brass tracery. The cover is inset with a brass escutcheon inscribed DONNE PAR LE ROI DES FRANÇAIS 1845. Both escutcheon and inlay are in rococo revival style. Green velvet lines the case; inside the top it is stamped in gold PRELAT BREVÉTÉ. À PARIS surrounded by ungilded rococo revival stampings. The pistols and their accessories are fitted into contoured compartments. The accessories include a wooden ramrod and a like cleaning rod, both with gilt-iron ferrules; a wooden mallet; a screwdriver with a wooden handle; and a two-piece wooden cap box. All wooden parts are artificially figured to imitate rosewood. There are also a polished iron bullet mold with sprue cutter, etched and damascened; a horn powder flask with a gilt metal powder measure; and an iron oil bottle. There are two covered compartments for loose accessories.

The Sotheby sale catalogue in which these pistols were last listed states that they were "Presented to the Governor of Malta by King Louis Philippe in 1845." Malta, however, was governed by a chief secretary until the appointment of its first governor, R. Moore O'Ferrall, in 1847. The presentation inscription gives no indication of the intended recipient of these pistols, whose initials may be presumed to be those that appear on the stock.

Provenance: Sotheby, November 30, 1962, lot 182.
Overall length, 15¼ in. (38.7 cm.); barrel, 10⅛ in. (25.7 cm.); caliber, .50

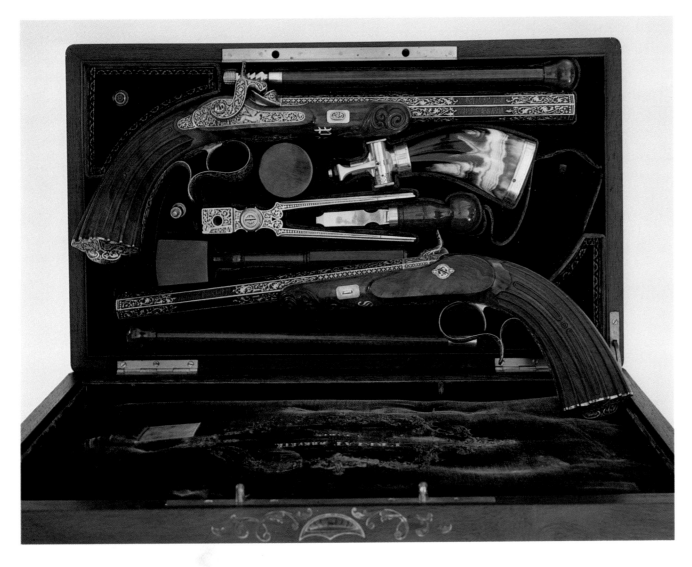

NETHERLANDISH

THE NETHERLANDS, originally part of the Habsburg inheritance, included modern Belgium. Technically, they were not politically divided until the Peace of the Hague in 1648, which finally separated the United Provinces in the north from Spanish Flanders in the south. Netherlandish firearms represent a stylistic middle ground between France and Germany.

In the early eighteenth century Belgian and Dutch arms form an amalgam of styles ranging from the Germanic to the more fashionable Parisian without fully embracing either extreme. It is a temptation to generalize that French design was more pleasing to French-speaking Belgians than it was to the Flemings or Dutch. In any event, Liège became the manufacturing center of French-oriented flintlock arms, although this style seems never to arrive intact simultaneously with its French counterpart. Several decades often separate the arms themselves from their decorative elements, which were conceived by Parisian designers.

Maastricht and Utrecht were the principal arms-making centers in the Netherlands and are known for their production of ivory-stocked pistols during the seventeenth century. Their arms production in general embodies more regional characteristics than that of Liège. This probably results from the influence of heavier German fashion in contrast to the lighter French taste.

24 Pair of Wheel-lock Pistols

DUTCH (?), ca. 1650

THE maple stocks are inlaid with staghorn scrolls, plaques, and borders. Opposite the locks are inlaid the engraved staghorn figures of Diana on one and Actaeon on the other. The full octagonal blued barrels are damascened at the extremes and midpoint. The blued locks have flat surfaces and external wheels, which are damascened around the arbor, and there is a damascened border around the lockplates. Their pans and covers are gilded. The locks are marked respectively with the stamped initials CK and HK on the inner surface of the plate. The iron pommels are damascened en suite with the lockplate borders, while the forend caps, ramrod tips, and thimbles are of gilded iron. The iron triggerguards are filed with simple moldings.

These pistols belong to a large group that are usually considered Dutch. Locks are characterized by fairly short, narrow tails, either flat or convex, and a small notched wheel retaining lug is positioned directly opposite the pan. The smallness of the locks probably relates to contemporary French wheel-locks, as does the inlaid decoration on the stocks of this pair.

Provenance: Parke-Bernet, New York (Edward H. Litchfield), December 5, 1961, lot 7; Sotheby, June 11, 1964, lot 44.
Overall length, 27½ in. (69.7 cm.); barrel, 19⅜ in. (49.2 cm.); caliber, .58

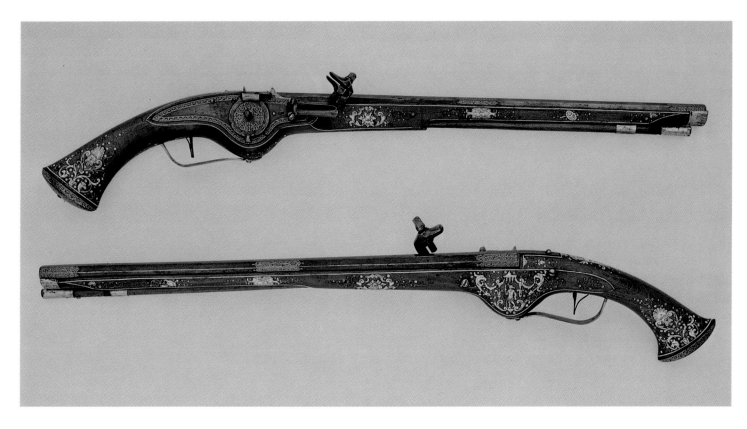

25 *Pair of Flintlock Pistols*

BELGIAN (LIÈGE), ca. 1670

THE ivory full stocks have a sculptured pommel in the shape of a laureled head separated by an ebony ring. The barrels are longitudinally ribbed and fluted for the breech third, become round following a heavy turned transition, and terminate in a reinforced muzzle. Flintlocks have engraved convex surfaces, and between the cock and battery spring are signed on the plate, CHARLE·FABRI. The plain iron mounts have convex surfaces, and there are two balustrate ramrod pipes.

The great majority of ivory-stocked pistols of this type come from Maastricht and its surrounding area (Aachen, Sedan, Liège), and Hayward records Fabri as working in Liège.[1] Dr. Lenk in *The Flintlock* makes a chronological study of the development of the sculptured pommel from the 1630s through the 1670s. Following his chronology, the relative smallness of the pommels of these pistols relates to similar pommels in use in Europe in the 1640s. However, both locks and triggerguards are consistent with those of Netherlandish arms of the 1660s. In the case of these pistols, the latest feature is the rear thimble with its attenuated tang indicating a date in the decade following 1665. While the most common form of the sculptured pommel is the helmeted head seen on the following pistols (No. 26), a variety of pommels were used from the second quarter of the seventeenth century. This variety exists not only in form—bird, animal, and human heads, both single and double—but also in material—cast brass, sheet silver, chiseled iron, ivory, and

ebony (for an earlier example, see No. 8). Not until the 1660s does the present combination of ivory pommel and stock become the norm. These ivory-stocked pistols are normally quite restrained in decoration thus emphasizing the richness of the ivory stock that terminates in the elaborately sculptured pommel, its artistic focal point.

Overall length, 18½ in. (47 cm.); barrel, 12 in. (30.5 cm.); caliber, .52

---

[1] Hayward, *Gunmaker*, II, p. 161.

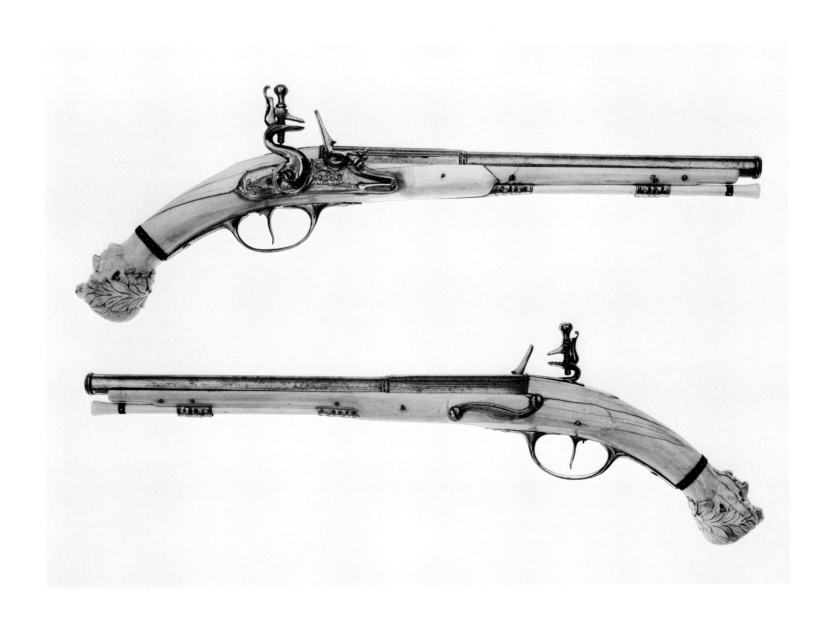

26 Pair of Flintlock Pistols

DUTCH (MAASTRICHT?), ca. 1670

THE ivory full stocks (now shortened) have floral carving around the tang and rear ramrod pipe. The helmeted head pommel has two transverse ebony bands at its juncture with the grip. The barrels are octagonal at the breech, make a gradual transition to a brief sixteen-sided section, and then become round following a ring turning. They were originally fitted with applied ring-turned muzzles that are now missing. The octagonal portion is lightly engraved on the upper flats. The locks have convex surfaces engraved with grotesques and foliage and are signed on the plate behind the cock (one of which is replaced) *C. Herold*. The plain iron mounts include two balustrate turned pipes.

The maker of the locks of these pistols was the same C. Herold of Dresden who signed in identical script the barrel of a wheel-lock rifle (107) in the James A. de Rothschild Collection.[1] The remainder of the workmanship is the same as that of pistols signed by J. Kosters of Maastricht. It would appear that Dresden locks were imported for use on these pistols rather than the Maastricht style being imitated in Dresden. This helmeted head pommel is identical in every detail to others on Kosters guns (for example, Tøjhusmuseet, Copenhagen, Nos. B. 920–921), thus suggesting the same workshop. Furthermore, the remarkable similarity between these Herold locks and some signed by Kosters may indicate that Kosters was applying his signature to Dresden locks. The shortened forends appear to have resulted from a modernization during the pistols' working life.

Overall length, 17½ in. (44.5 cm.); barrel, 11 3/16 in. (28.2 cm.); caliber, .48

---

[1] Claude Blair, *Arms, Armour and Base-Metalwork: The James A. de Rothschild Collection at Waddesdon Manor* (Fribourg: Published for the National Trust by Office du Livre, 1974), p. 277.

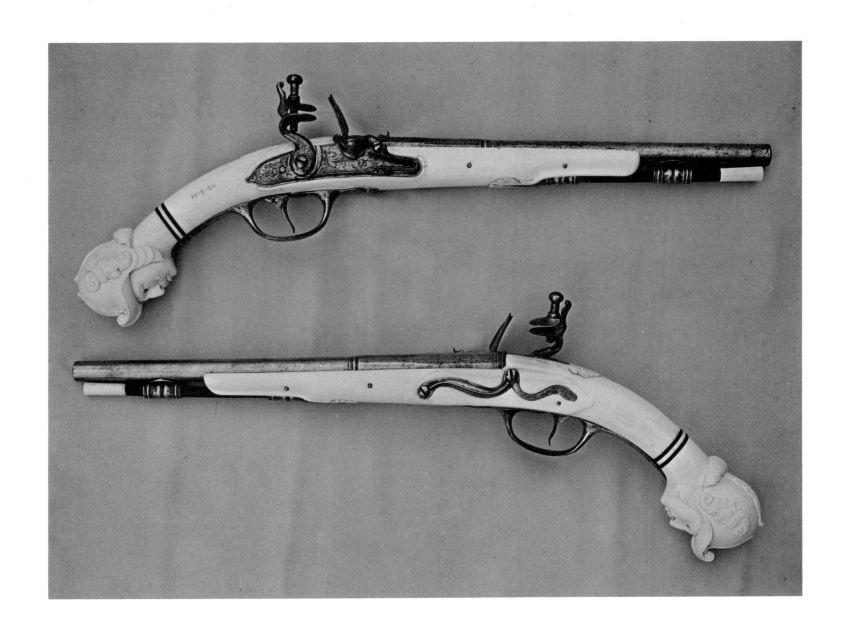

27 Pair of Flintlock Pistols

DUTCH (UTRECHT), ca. 1680

THE stump walnut stocks have relief-carved foliage and borders. The barrels are divided into four sections and are chiseled in relief. They are octagonal at the breech, turning to sixteen-sided, followed by a short round segment enclosed by ring moldings, and a plain round section continuing to the muzzle. The locks have convex surfaces with engraving on the plate and relief chiseling on the cock and battery. The goddess Cybele is engraved on the plate forward of the cock. Below is the engraved signature IAN·KNOOP·UTRECHT. The mounts are iron with the sideplate and escutcheon relief chiseled and pierced. The triggerguard and pommel are relief chiseled and the latter terminates in a Medusa head. Two baluster-turned pipes hold the horn ramrod.

Jan Knoop has been recognized as the outstanding Dutch gunmaker working in Holland during the seventeenth century. However, he was certainly surpassed by his contemporary Adriaen Reynier, known as le Hollandois, who emigrated to Paris. The majority of existing Knoop firearms seems to have been produced for foreign, especially Scandinavian, patronage; among Knoop's clients was King Charles XI of Sweden. In spite of working in the most modern French fashion, Knoop curiously was one of the last producers of wheel-locks in Holland. These Dutch pistols represent the extension of the Louis XIV classical style into which, in this instance, Knoop has incorporated certain foreign elements. In both the iron chiseling and the stock carving, the repeated use of the broad naturalistic leaf has no counterpart in French academic design and may have its origin in folk art. The pommels with their two-stage spurs are unusual, but are also characteristic of Utrecht pistols and appear to represent the combining of the earlier short-spurred pommel with the later long-spurred one.

Initially these pistols appear to be somewhat earlier than their assigned date, but the elaboration of the carving around the rear pipe and barrel tang together with the bulbous relief molding bordering the pommel are developments belonging to the 1680s. The small carved mask with silver eyes just to the rear of the barrel tang is remarkably similar to that of the much later Leopold Becher pistols (No. 65).

Provenance: Joe Kindig, Jr., York, Pennsylvania, 1969.
Overall length, 19¼ in. (48.8 cm.); barrel, 12⅝ in. (32 cm.); caliber, .65

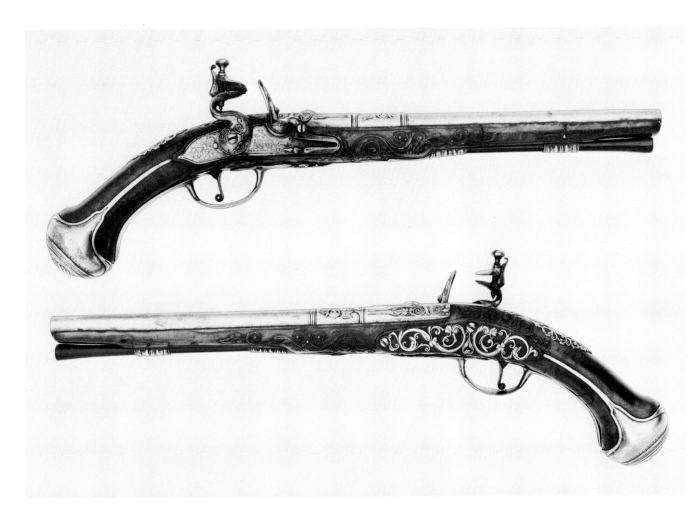

28 *Pair of Flintlock Pistols*

DUTCH, ca. 1680

THE stocks of medium quality stump walnut are lightly carved with foliage and molded borders. The round barrels, with sighting ribs that stop just short of the muzzle, have elongated front sights. The breech has two raised side flats that run a short distance down the barrel. The humped tang is hollowed forming a short open rear sight. Lock surfaces are convex and are engraved with foliage incorporating grotesque heads and a human half-figure. The front of the battery is chiseled in relief. The signature GRVCHÉ A PARIS is engraved along the lower edge of the plate in front of the cock. The mounts are iron; the escutcheon and sideplate are pierced and chiseled in relief. Foliate finials terminate the triggerguard, and two bulbous turned thimbles hold the ramrod, while the spurred pommels end in a chiseled mask.

The signature GRVCHÉ A PARIS on the lockplates in this case does not necessarily indicate that the entire pistols were manufactured at Paris. Certainly these locks are not as opulent as those usually associated with this maker, but their quality is high and there is no reason to doubt their origin. On the other hand, the quality of the chiseled and engraved mounts is greatly inferior to that of the locks. While competent, the stocking displays bulbous carving around the rear pipe more often associated with Netherlandish arms. Also Netherlandish are the humped tang rear sight and the very elongated foresight at an exaggerated distance from the muzzle. A hunting horn mark on the underside of each barrel breech, while partly obliterated, appears to be that shown in Støckel as 5232 or 5233, which he associates with Holland. In view of the discrepancy in quality and their strong Netherlandish features, the obvious conclusion is that these pistols were built around Paris locks. The exportation of locks and barrels by internationally renowned masters was a common practice in the seventeenth and eighteenth centuries.

Gruché was one of the leading Paris gunmakers of the seventeenth century. Several surviving examples of his work are of the highest quality and are as lavish in their detail as any produced in that period. Two of these guns are illustrated in Lenk, *Flintlock*, pl. 77, and a pair of pistols of very fine quality in the Odescalchi Collection at Rome are pictured in Carpegna's catalogue of that collection, pp. 104–108 and facing p. 131. Hayward states that Louis XIV appears to have commissioned Gruché to produce pieces for royal presentation, a fact that indicates the high contemporary esteem his arms enjoyed.[1] He also identifies him as a Huguenot and places him in London in 1699 when a *Pierre Le Sieur Gruché* is recorded as having married at the Huguenot Church at Hungerford market.[2] Gruché can have been no younger than his middle fifties at that time. There are no known English arms from his hand.

Provenance: Geoffrey Jenkinson, London, 1970.
Overall length, 23⅝ in. (60 cm.); barrel, 17⅛ in. (43.5 cm.); caliber, .63

---

[1] Hayward, *Gunmaker*, II, pp. 45–46.
[2] J. F. Hayward, "The Huguenot Gunmakers of London," *Journal of the Arms & Armour Society*, VI (December 1968), p. 121.

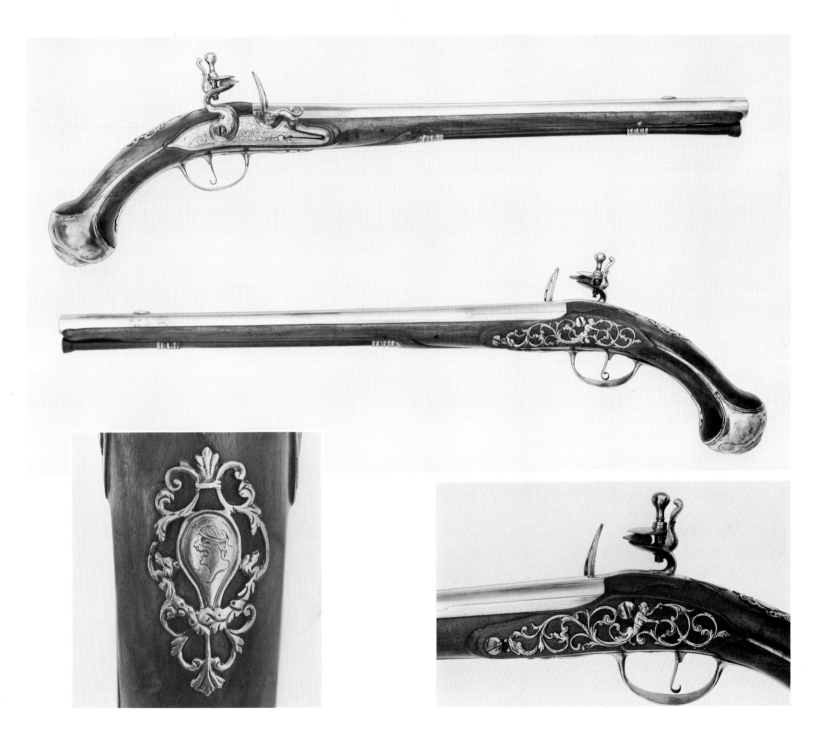

29 Flintlock Pistol

BELGIAN (LIÈGE), ca. 1715

THE walnut stock is relief carved with foliage and borders and terminates in a dark horn tip. The barrel is octagonal for a short portion of the breech, and round for the remainder of its length. A putto in low relief with a small amount of damascening and engraving precedes a raised sighting rib signed in inlaid gold, İ·B·İACQVET·A·LİEGE. The hollowed humped tang serves as a rear sight, and there is an elongated front sight. Two unidentified marks are stamped under the breech. The flat surfaces of the lock are chiseled and engraved, and the signature İ·B·İACQVET appears in the center of the plate. The pierced iron sideplate and other mounts are chiseled and engraved, are highlighted with small amounts of damascening, and are inlaid with gold beads. The original ramrod terminates in a horn tip matching the forend cap.

This pistol adheres closely to the Louis XIV classical style. However, the flat surfaces of the lockplate and the faceted ramrod pipes are of the newer "Bérain" style first published by de la Collombe in 1705 (see Piraube, No. 12). The inlaid gold beads and the slight damascened areas highlighting the chiseled steel are a technique used by Piraube and Gruché in Paris and Bongarde in Düsseldorf. The decorative use of gold was not expressed in the pattern books; therefore, this unusually individual treatment employing restrained gold accents probably indicates some association between these makers. Other features, however, such as the humped tang rear sight, the large elongated foresight, the heavy upturned battery foot, and the extensive reel and bead engraving, are quite typical of Liège-made firearms.

Provenance: Arthur Yates, Costa Mesa, California, 1964.
Overall length, 22¼ in. (56.5 cm.); barrel, 15½ in. (39.3 cm.); caliber, .69

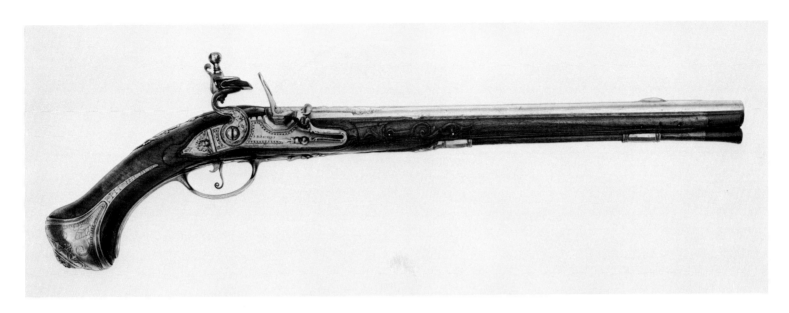

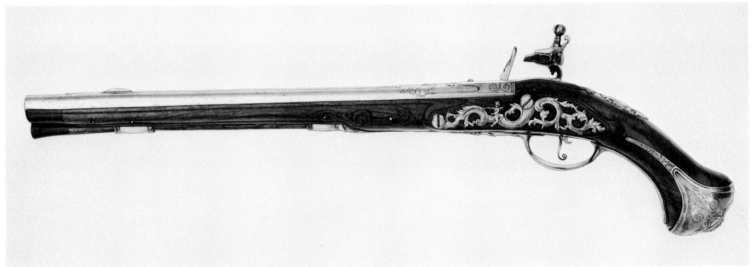

30 *Pair of Flintlock Pistols*

BELGIAN (LIÈGE), ca. 1715

THIS pair of stump walnut stocked pistols have blued barrels in two stages. The octagonal breech is stamped with the spurious mark of Alonso Martínez and his countermark, a dog (like Støckel 752, 753, and 759). Following a transitional acanthus leaf frieze, the remainder of the barrel is round. There is a silver blade front sight. The lock has flat surfaces, is chiseled in low relief, and is signed DEVILLERS along its lower beveled edge. The cock is chiseled en suite with the lockplate, and the forward face of the battery is chiseled with a mask and foliate scrolls. The cock of the lower pistol is a modern replacement. Mounts are of gilt brass. The spurred pommel terminates in a mask surrounded by an acanthus leaf frieze. Surmounted by a crown, the escutcheon has two dogs as supporters and terminates in a mask. The chased sideplate shows a seated Diana surrounded by foliage and piercings.

Liège-made firearms by masters such as Devillers and Gilles de Selier followed the French fashion. Their makers seem to have utilized Parisian patterns such as those by Nicolas Guérard (d. 1719), possibly in pirated editions by Weigel and Raab. This pair by Devillers was strongly influenced by Guérard's designs, while other features such as the lockplate profile and some of the grotesque masks are survivals of the late seventeenth century.

The use of counterfeit Alonso Martínez barrels illustrates the international popularity of Madrid barrels, which at that time were recognized as being superior to those available in other European countries. Alonso Martínez studied in Madrid under the royal gunsmith, Juan Belén (d. 1691). He worked in Portugal during the first years of the eighteenth century, transferred to Barcelona ca. 1710, and ended his life as master of the arms factory of Mallorca. While the counterfeiting of Spanish barrels was common in Europe toward the middle of the eighteenth century, this is a particularly early example of the practice. It is interesting to note that Martínez was still active at the time when these fraudulent barrels were produced.

Provenance: One pistol is from Joe Kindig, Jr., York, Pennsylvania; its mate is from W. Keith Neal, Warminster, England, 1961.
Overall length, 19½ in. (49.5 cm.); barrel, 12½ in. (31.7 cm.); caliber, .65

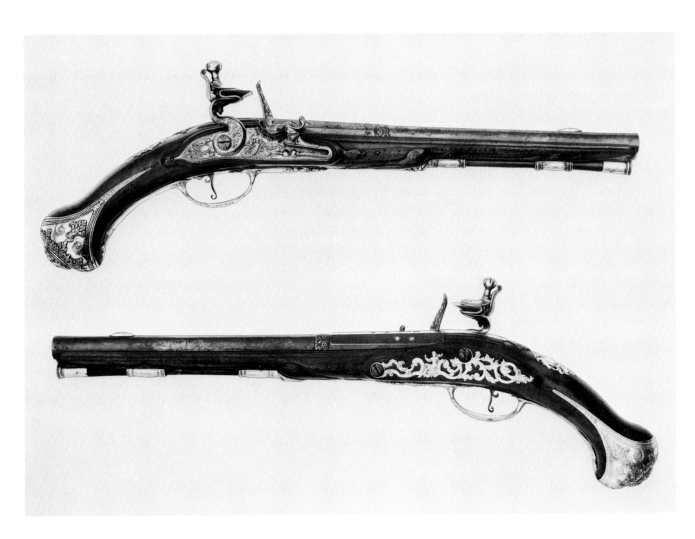

31 *Flintlock Pistol*

BELGIAN (LIÈGE), ca. 1725

THE carved stump walnut stock is mounted with a round barrel that is octagonal only at the extreme breech. A sighting rib stops just short of the elongated engraved silver front sight. A raised portion of the chased and engraved silver barrel tang forms a shallow rear sight. The barrel tang is held from below by a screw whose head is flush with the trigger plate. The gunsmith's mark, a rampant lion, struck in gold, appears on each of the three upper breech flats. The lock, signed G. DESELIER, has a combination of convex and faceted surfaces that are chiseled in low relief with engraved borders. The top jaw screw and the spur of the cock are replacements. The silver mounts, cast in relief, are chased and engraved.

This arm relates closely in style to the two preceding Liège pistols. The combination of convex and faceted lock elements, the lockplate profile, the heavy flange at the base of the pan, the strongly upturned battery foot, the florid engraving with heavy leafage, the reel and bead lockplate border that is repeated on the pommel spur, the raised sight on the tang with its bulbous wood surround, the elongated front sight, and the deeply cutout rear extension of the trigger are all characteristic of Liège guns of the early eighteenth century. These features are not exclusive to Liège, but are characteristics shared by the Dutch and Flemish gunmaking schools. The lockplate contour and profile, the balustrate thimbles, and the form of the barrel all relate to Parisian arms design of almost a half-century earlier, while the trigger is reminiscent of that of French arms of ca. 1660. While Støckel (1018, 1019) lists these barrel marks as those of Gilles de Selier II and places him in Paris, the pistol has little relationship to Paris work of this time period. Støckel, however, does show Gilles I as working in Liège at the close of the seventeenth century.

Provenance: Geoffrey Jenkinson, London, 1967.
Overall length, 20 in. (50.8 cm.); barrel, 13⅜ in. (34.5 cm.); caliber, .62

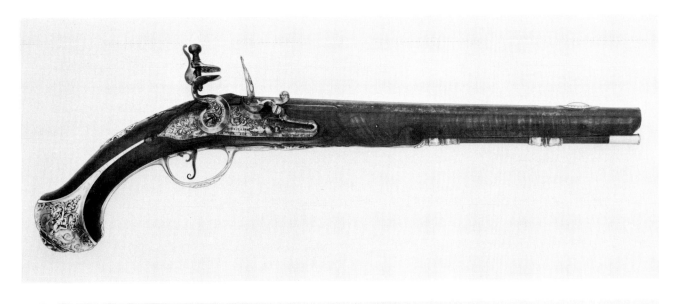

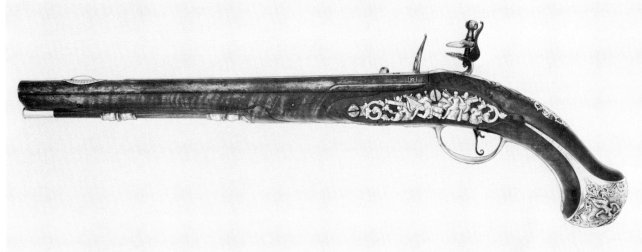

32 Cased Pinfire Double-Barreled Shotgun

BELGIAN (BRUSSELS), 1866

THE two-piece walnut stock has a checkered grip and forend. Double damascus barrels are signed in gold along the sighting rib AD. JANSEN ARQUEBUSIER DU ROI A BRUX-ELLES. The locks are delicately engraved with hounds, pheasants, and hares. The mounts, locks, and breech block are gold overlaid in foliate and scrolled symmetrical designs on a mat and blue ground. The Belgian royal arms containing the Order of the Garter are just forward of the trigger-guard. A round brass plaque inlaid in the top of the rosewood case also bears the royal arms and the inscription, DONNÉ PAR LE ROI DES BELGES A SIR CHARLES GEORGE YOUNG ROI D'ARMES DU TRÉS NOBLE ORDRE DE LA JARRETIÈRE ("Given by the King of the Belgians to Sir Charles George Young, King of Arms of the Most Noble Order of the Garter"). The case is lined with blue velvet on which the maker's name is stamped in gold. Contained in the case with the shotgun are the following accessories: two reloading tools, a shot measure, a powder measure, a three-part ebony rod, a case-hardened mainspring vise, and two screwdrivers. All of the turned handles are ebony, and all of the brass is gilded. A leather case contains twelve pinfire shotgun shells. A brass swab tip, an iron wire brush, and a wool swab are in a closed compartment. An accompanying printed program announcing the investiture of Leopold II of Belgium dates this gun 1866.

Provenance: W. Keith Neal, Warminster, England, 1964.
Overall length, 46⅝ in. (117 cm.); barrel, 29½ in. (75 cm.); gauge, 12

[82]

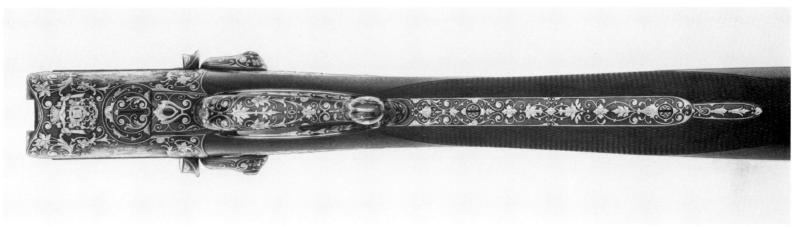

DURING the period covered by the arms in this collection, tremendous changes can be seen in English gun making. In the middle of the seventeenth century English firearms tended to be severe, their style generally Continental in origin combining Netherlandish and French influences. Arms made during this time not only display these influences but have combined elements showing as much as twenty to thirty years chronological disparity. An excellent example of this combination of disparate elements is a flintlock rifled carbine by E. Truelocke of ca. 1670 in the Colonial Williamsburg Collection (illustrated in Sotheby [William G. Renwick Collection, Pt. I], July 17, 1972, lot 22). The style of its metal parts, and their chiseled and engraved decoration, are in the contemporary fashion of Thuraine and le Hollandois, while the form of the buttstock and its grotesque carving are similar to the Western Europe group (1640–1650). Truelocke was a leading gunmaker; this carbine is one of the finest extant English firearms of his day. More ordinary arms of the period show an even greater time span in their elements.

English gunmaking during the latter half of the seventeenth century attracted numerous workmen from the Continent, but the great influx occurred following the revocation of the Edict of Nantes in 1685. Then, for the first time, there came from France not only outstanding provincial makers but Parisian gunsmiths of international renown. Their arrival created a renaissance of gunmaking which, however, was neither universal nor immediate. The refined Louis XIV classical style clashed with the entrenched archaic fashion of the native English gunmakers. The London Gunmakers' Company openly opposed and harassed the Huguenot immigrants. In spite of this, many acquired royal and noble patrons and, as a consequence, were able to work outside the restrictions of the Company. While this freedom allowed them to work in the Louis XIV classical style, they encountered another barrier in the conservatism of even their noble patrons. In fact, the Parisian gunsmith Monlong produced in London the superb pair of pistols possibly made for William III (reigned 1689–1702), now in the Tower of London (illustrated in Hayward, *Gunmaker,* II, pls. 17–18). These Monlong pistols with their heavily voluted and chiseled cock and battery and pierced trigger are made precisely in the Thuraine and le Hollandois style used by Monlong in France in the 1660s. This obviously deliberate step backward is easily seen when one compares them with those made in the latest style by Monlong and Frappier in Paris to be given in 1673 to Charles XI of Sweden (Stockholm, Livrustkammaren, 12/24). By comparing these pieces with other English firearms of the assimilated Louis XIV classical style, one can only conclude that a substantial lag must be taken into account when dating English arms according to stylistic development.

The eighteenth century saw a continuation of the Louis XIV fashion to the exclusion of the "Bérain" style with its flat surfaces. The rounded forms endured until mid-century when they were gradually replaced. During the second half of the eighteenth century, the English took over the leading role in the development of the flintlock. This leadership was in mechanical development and excellence in finish and workmanship. Mechanical refinements include the rainproof pan and the friction roller on the battery spring.

33 Dog-lock Pistol

ENGLISH, ca. 1660

THE rosewood full stock has relief carving around the tang. The barrel has a short octagonal breech that becomes sixteen-sided, then turns to round following a faceted girdle. It is rifled with eight grooves and has the London proofs and a star-shaped maker's mark struck in the breech. Engraved tulips and acanthus leaves cover the breech and a small area at the muzzle. The engraved flat lock has an external dog catch for half cock. The button trigger is of iron. There is an engraved silver band at the forend tip, and the silver butt-cap is engraved and pierced.

The English are not noted for the production of rifled firearms, but for a brief period around the middle of the seventeenth century rifling did enjoy considerable popularity. While this pistol is rifled, it is otherwise a conventional muzzle loader in contrast to the majority of English rifled arms of the day that were turn-off breechloaders.

The date given to this diminutive pistol is based on the form of the lockplate, battery, and battery spring, which are depicted in the pattern book by Jacquinet, who illustrated designs by Thuraine and le Hollandois (1660). Its other features, however, relate to a decade earlier.

Provenance: R. W. MacWillie, Lakewood, California.
Overall length, 9¾ in. (24.8 cm.); barrel, 5⅜ in. (13.6 cm.); caliber, .46

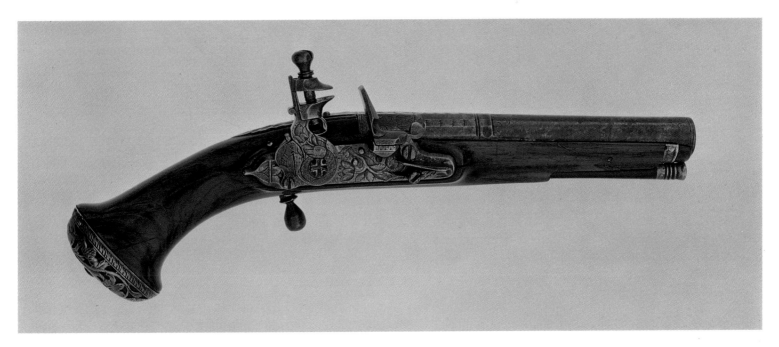

34 *Pair of Flintlock Turn-off Pistols*

ENGLISH (LONDON), ca. 1695

HALF-STOCKS of burl maple have relief-carved borders and silver wire inlay. The barrels are in three stages: octagonal at the engraved breech with chiseled panels forming a gradual transition to ring turnings, the two round forward sections—the rear engraved—are separated by turnings, and the muzzle is reinforced. The barrels, rifled with six grooves, unscrew for loading at the first turned section; just forward of this on the underside is a small lug for the spanner. The convex flintlocks have relief-chiseled cock and battery, while the plate is engraved with grotesques and foliate scrolls. The engraved signature DOLEP is forward of the cock and is partially hidden under the finial of the battery spring (one finial is missing). The sideplates are pierced and chiseled in relief. The iron triggerguards and pommels are engraved and lightly chiseled. The escutcheons are chiseled with the Medici arms surmounted by a ducal crown over a grotesque mask—all with damascened gold highlights.

Andrew Dolep's origins are uncertain. He was a "Dutchman" of German or Netherlandish origin who is known to have been working in London by 1681. In that year he was refused admission to the Gunmaker's Company, perhaps for being a foreigner. It is significant that in 1689 he was admitted freeman after having acquired as his patron the Master of the Ordinance, Lord Dartmouth. He died in 1713.

Most important of all of Dolep's surviving works is the set of firearms perhaps presented by Charles II or William III to a member or members of the family of Cosimo III, Grand Duke of Tuscany, of which these pistols apparently formed a part. The gift consisted of a fowler now in the Armeria

Reale, Turin, a pair of pocket pistols at Capodimonte, Naples, these pistols, and a set of pocket tools in the Tower of London. These firearms, while not decorated en suite, all bear the Medici arms. Furthermore, the fowler has the silver wire mirror cipher FM in the buttstock, hence the recipient of the gift is presumed to have been either the Grand Duke's younger brother, Francesco Maria dei Medici (1660–1711), or more probably Cosimo's eldest son, Ferdinando (1663–1713).

The date given these pistols is somewhat later than that usually assigned to the set. Certainly they have a number of early features, many of which date from the 1660s, which include the grotesques on the lockplate of the pistols and the highly foliate masks engraved on the barrel, both from the period of Thuraine and le Hollandois. The barrel damascening of the fowler at Turin is likewise consistent with this period. However, there is at least one feature that is not encountered before the 1680s. Most significant is the manner of the silver stock inlay in which the earlier use of engraved sheet has been virtually eschewed in favor of the new method of using multiple parallel pieces of silver wire to form the heavier portions of the inlaid design. Dr. Lenk traces the development of this technique to Paris-made arms of the late 1680s. Since it does not appear in published patterns until 1693, one should not expect this style to appear in England before well into the 1690s. A somewhat later English example of the same technique, possibly by the same stocker, may be seen in the Barbar pistols in this collection (No. 35).

The pistols are cased in a velvet-lined Florentine leather

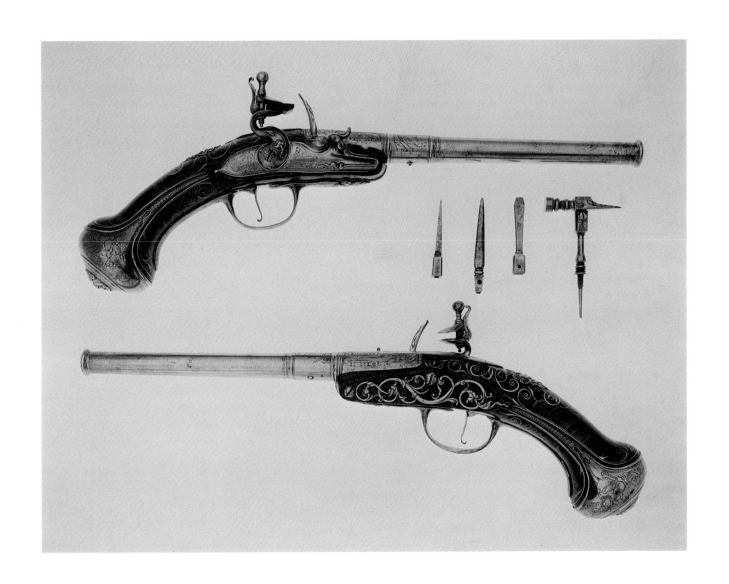

box dating from the late nineteenth century. The accompanying combination tools are possibly of the pistols' period, but are not associated. The engraved monogram WR(?) is engraved on the handle of the hammer.

Provenance: Cranbrook Academy of Arts, Bloomfield Hills, Michigan; Sotheby, May 15, 1972, lot 306.
Overall length, 15⅝ in. (39.7 cm.); barrel, 9⅝ in. (24.5 cm.); caliber, .50

34

34

35 *Pair of Flintlock Pistols*

ENGLISH (LONDON), ca. 1705

THE full stocks of matched stump walnut have borders and foliage in relief and silver wire inlay. The barrels have a short engraved octagonal section at the breech followed by a relief-chiseled transition to round that ends in turnings and an acanthus leaf girdle. The round forward section has an iron front sight and is engraved with the arms of Georg Ludwig, Duke of Hesse-Darmstadt (1668–1705) surrounded by the collar of the Golden Fleece. The inscription BARBAR· LONDINI is engraved on the upper breech; three illegible marks are in the position of barrel proofs. The locks are convex, relief chiseled, and engraved. The engraved signature BARBAR·LONDINI appears along the lower edge of the plate. The iron sideplate is chiseled and pierced. Remaining iron mounts are chiseled and engraved, and the escutcheons carry the engraved number 45. There are two balustrate ramrod pipes.

Lewis Barbar (Barbier?) was born in "Essendon" (probably Issoudun in Berry), France. He was a Huguenot, and is recorded as working in England in 1698, when he was fined on August 25 for possessing unproved barrels. He was naturalized on April 4, 1700, and was admitted to the Gunmakers' Company on July 14, 1704. On April 13, 1717, he received the appointment of Gentleman Armourer to King George I. Barbar remained in this post after the accession of George II, serving until his death in May 1741. He appears to be the first of several generations of Barbars who worked in London during the eighteenth century.[1]

---

[1] W. Keith Neal and D. H. L. Back, *Great British Gunmakers, 1740–1790: The History of John Twigg and the Packington Guns* (London: Sotheby Parke Bernet Productions, 1975), pp. 102–103.

It can be presumed that Lewis Barbar arrived in England an accomplished gunsmith. However, despite our knowledge of his place of birth, there is no indication as to where in France he received his training or established his practice prior to his departure. He is not recorded as working in Paris, and it is more likely that he was established in a provincial town. If this was true, as indeed it was in the case of many other prominent Huguenot gunmakers—and considering that Barbar became gunsmith to George I—it graphically demonstrates the high standard of workmanship achieved in France during the period dominated by the classical Louis XIV style. The advantage enjoyed by Barbar and his peers over their native English urban counterparts is a commentary on the relatively unsophisticated state of English gunmaking at that time.

These pistols, as well as other arms by Lewis Barbar, are stocked in stump walnut at a time when burl maple was the predominant stock wood for fine English arms. Barbar seems to have followed the fashion of Piraube, who consistently used stump walnut when other Paris makers were employing both woods. Also consistent with the French style, Barbar has executed a very slight swell with volute carving in the stock at the rear pipe that contrasts with the London fashion, in which a large bulbous swell is accentuated by a deeply carved serpentine line. This latter treatment is more related to Dutch and German arms than to French.

The arms of Georg Ludwig, Duke of Hesse-Darmstadt, which are engraved on the barrels provide the latest date for these pistols. A further clue to their date is supplied by the apparently fraudulent barrel marks, which seem to be

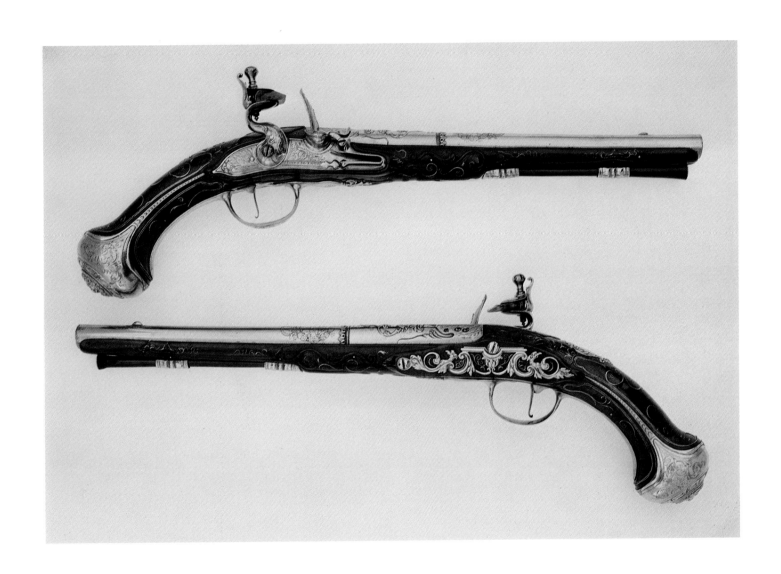

a loose imitation of the London Gunmakers' Company proofs. Barbar was not admitted to the Company until July 14, 1704, and it is improbable that he would have used such marks after that date.

These pistols, which the evidence seems to date prior to 1704, may possibly be the earliest documented arms by Lewis Barbar. They are certainly among the finest of his existing works.

Provenance: F. Theodore Dexter, Pasadena, California; Charles H. Moses, Ashtabula, Ohio, 1966.
Overall length, 19⅛ in. (48.5 cm.); barrel, 12¼ in. (31 cm.); caliber, .64

35

35

36 *Pair of Flintlock Pistols*

ENGLISH (DONCASTER), ca. 1715

THE burl maple full stocks have borders in relief and engraved sheet silver inlay. Their round barrels are in two stages: the breech is relief chiseled and engraved and bears the arms of Bagshaw; the forward stage has a raised sighting rib engraved HENRY ELLIS IN DONCASTER that carries the silver blade front sight. The flintlocks are relief chiseled and engraved and bear the signature H. ELLIS along the lower edge of the plate. The pan is made with a bridle that retains a battery pivot screw entering from the interior of the plate. The silver mounts are chased and engraved; both pommels and escutcheons also carry the Bagshaw arms. The ramrod pipes have bulbous turnings. The wooden ramrods have a burl maple tip, matching the stock wood, which terminates in an iron plate.

Besides a number of existing guns by Henry Ellis, there is but a single contemporary reference to him, an indenture of lease dated April 18, 1712, for a dwelling house in the borough of Doncaster.

Hayward has illustrated one of a pair of pistols signed by Ellis in the Dinely Collection on which he points out that some of the barrel design and stock inlay derive from pls. 5 and 6 of Simonin's 1685 pattern book. This French influence has been further pursued by A. D. Darling, who has used arms by Ellis to illustrate the influence of the classical Louis XIV style on English provincial gunmaking.[1] While

Darling has concentrated on Doncaster as the source of Ellis's arms, a careful study of the group raises serious questions regarding this thesis. The virtually identical chiseling on the cocks of these pistols and on those of a pair by James Ermendinger, also in the Bedford Collection (Metropolitan Museum exhibit, No. 12), indicates that Ellis was possibly availing himself of the same iron chiseler, if not the same London lockmaker. The consistently good quality of Ellis's silver mounts is to be expected, since it was standard practice for English makers to acquire their mounts from silversmiths. On these pistols, the workmanship of the silver plaques inlaid in the stocks is inferior in quality to that of the mounts, and more especially to the locks. Having to be engraved after mounting, these plaques would have fallen into the province of the gunstocker. The similarity of design between them and those of the somewhat older Dinely pistols appears to indicate the same hand, but here it exhibits a noticeable decline in concept and engraving. This decline is also to be seen in the case of the barrel chiseling, but over the same time span the quality of the locks and mounts does not exhibit any such decline, thereby providing further evidence of a division of labor. It is inconceivable, moreover, that the engraver of these locks could have had a hand in engraving either this inlay or these mounts.

The date of these pistols is based on the relatively late design of the sideplate, which is found in hallmarked examples during the period 1715–1720, on the fully developed lock molding with its extended tab ending, and on the small grip of the stock, which gives a pronounced flair to the pommel.

---

[1] Anthony D. Darling, "English Provincial Gunmaking, 1680–1720, as Exemplified by Some Works of Henry Ellis of Doncaster," in Robert Held, ed., *Arms and Armor Annual*, I (Chicago: Follett Publishing Co., 1973), pp. 196–205.

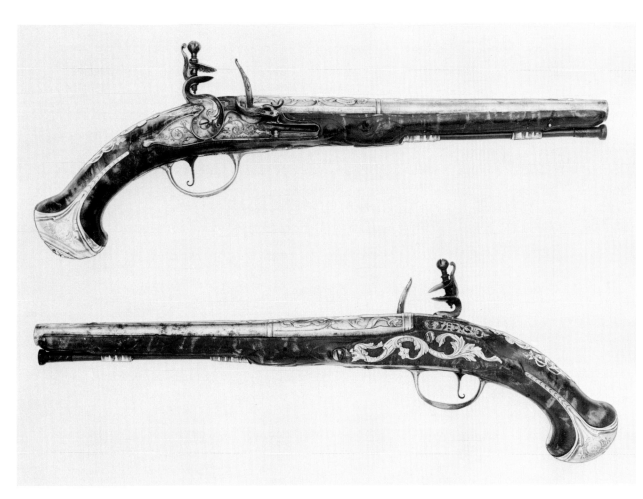

Provenance: Geoffrey Jenkinson, London, 1969.
Overall length, 18¾ in. (47.6 cm.); barrel, 12 in. (30.5 cm.); caliber, .60

37 *Flintlock Gun*

ENGLISH (LONDON), ca. 1720

THE stump walnut full stock is inlaid with silver wire and is carved with geometric and leaf designs. The barrel, octagonal at the extreme breech, makes a transition to a short sixteen-sided section, then continues round to a slightly flared muzzle with an iron foresight. A slash in the tang and barrel breech forms the rear sight. The breech is relief chiseled en suite with the stock carving, and has floral and border engraving. The left side is struck with two partly obliterated oval marks, which appear to be London view and proof marks. The engraved inscription HUTCHINSON LONDINI is divided by the rear sight. The lock with convex surfaces has relief chiseling on the battery, raised borders on the cock and lockplate, and the remainder is engraved with line borders and floral designs. W. HUTCHINSON is engraved within a floral cartouche in the center of the plate. An external safety is behind the cock. The iron mounts are relief chiseled and engraved. Military trophies are engraved on the tang of the buttplate. There are four balustrate ramrod pipes (of which the forward three have been replaced along with a section of the forend). The chased silver escutcheon is in the shape of a thistle.

This appears to be the first documentation of W. Hutchinson,[1] of whom one other gun and a rifle are known. Considering the ambitiousness and fine quality of this gun, it is surprising that other examples have not surfaced.

This gun provides a remarkable example of the Louis XIV classical style's tenacity in England long after its demise in France, where the new "Bérain" fashion, with its flat and faceted surfaces, had replaced it a good decade earlier. In spite of their awareness of this change, the English continued to cling doggedly to the archaic round surfaces until about the middle of the eighteenth century. Proof of their awareness of the new style is seen on many English firearms of the period. It is well demonstrated by the adoption of the "Bérain" signature cartouche on the lock and the "Bérain" style wire stock inlay on the gun illustrated. This style replaced engraved sheet silver with designs formed only of silver wire. The naive quality of the wire ornament of this gun shows that the stocker was not working from published designs but more likely had been exposed to arms by Continental or immigrant Huguenot gunsmiths. Two pistols by the London gunsmith Richard Sinckler,[2] one hallmarked 1717 and the other 1720, have wire inlay whose design and execution is strikingly similar to that of the above gun. The similarity is so marked that it may indicate the same stocker.

A gun similar to this is in the W. Keith Neal Collection, Warminster, England; a turn-off rifled carbine, also signed W. HUTCHINSON, is in the collection of Colonial Williamsburg. It bears the arms of John Murray, Earl of Dunmore, last colonial governor of Virginia. The barrel carries the London proofs and the foreigners' mark, thus establishing the date of its manufacture as post-1741. This indicates a long productive span making the scarcity of Hutchinson's arms all the more puzzling.

---

[1] J. N. George, *English Guns and Rifles* (Harrisburg, Pa.: The Stackpole Co., 1947), lists a Hutchinson as working in London ca. 1700–1725, but gives no textual reference.

[2] Metropolitan Museum of Art, *Early Firearms of Great Britain and Ireland from the Collection of Clay P. Bedford* (Greenwich, Conn.: New York Graphic Society, 1971), pls. 21–22.

Provenance: Robert E. Perkins, Mobile, Alabama, 1972.
Overall length, 57½ in. (146.2 cm.); barrel, 41½ in. (105.6 cm.);
caliber, .71

38 *Highland Lock Pistol of Scottish Form*

ENGLISH (LONDON), ca. 1770

THE silver gilt stock is chased in relief within engraved moldings. The round iron barrel has ring moldings at the breech followed by a short longitudinally ribbed section. Ring moldings enclose relief-chiseled panels, and the flared muzzle terminates in an octagon. A rear sight is notched into the breech molding. Two private London proof marks are struck in the left side of the breech. The convex lock surfaces are relief chiseled and signed CHRISTI LONDON (for a description of the Highland lock, see No. 39). The ball trigger is silver gilt and matches the head of the pricker. The iron belthook is inlaid with gold, and its attachment finial is pierced and engraved. The original iron ramrod is turned and is retained by a single long engraved pipe. The two gold plaques in the butt are defaced by more recent diaper engraving.

This pistol is by the same hand that produced the quite similar, but somewhat richer, pistol of George III, signed JON. CHRISTIE · STIRLING, now in the royal collection at Windsor Castle. It has not been ascertained whether this maker is the same John Christie who worked—possibly some years earlier—in Doune, where several generations of this gunmaking family are recorded. The signature on this arm indicates that John Christie of Stirling transferred to London after the presentation of the Windsor pistol, possibly as a result of royal favor. The academic rococo decoration of this pistol, in contrast to the one at Windsor, which has a traditional "celtic" ornament, must reflect the result of Christie's removal to London.

Evidence points to this pistol also having been made for King George III. Not only are the two arms related through the unique extravagance of their silver stocks, but both also have a thistle surmounted by the royal crown on the stock directly behind the breech. On both pistols the chiseled iron-work on lock and barrel is closely related. Furthermore, the inlaid butt plaques of this pistol have been resurfaced and engraved to obliterate the original design, the ghost image of which remains, especially on the reverse plaque. The corresponding plaques on the Windsor pistol bear the royal cipher, crown, and garter. If such arms existed on this piece, they undoubtedly would have been removed at the time it left the royal collection.

Provenance: Frank Horner, Madison, Wisconsin, 1969.
Overall length, 11⅝ in. (29.5 cm.); barrel, 7³⁄₁₆ in. (17.8 cm.); caliber, .53

39 *Pair of Highland Lock Pistols*

SCOTTISH (DOUNE), ca. 1780

THE iron stocks have ramshorn butts inlaid with gold and silver wire and retain traces of their original blue. The barrels are round and have an elevated ring turning at the breech that is notched for a rear sight. The longitudinally ribbed breech turns to round at the midsection and becomes octagonal at the muzzle. The two forward sections are engraved. The flat-surfaced locks are engraved, and the signature *John Campbell* appears on the plate between the cock and battery spring. Both trigger and pricker heads are gold. The engraved iron belthooks have filed moldings and pierced terminals. Plain gold plaques are inlaid in the sides of the butt, and the iron ramrods are retained by a single iron pipe.

There were three generations of Campbells working in Doune, and their productivity spans the entire eighteenth century. This John Campbell appears to have worked during the second half of the century, and these pistols certainly fall within its final quarter. This date is indicated by the form of the cock and its molding, the shallow rainproof pan with its rounded cover, and the tendency toward the late right-angled butt. The nature of the barrel engraving with its profusion of shaded areas suggests the influence of bright-cut technique, which was popular in English neoclassical silver. One pistol of this pair, or an exact duplicate, is described and illustrated in Whitelaw's treatise.[1]

In contrast to the conventional flintlock, these pistols are fitted with the so-called Highland lock in which the single sear pivots horizontally through a hole in the lockplate at half-cock to engage the breast of the cock; at full cock it engages the internal tumbler. The metal ramshorn stock is the type most associated with Scottish pistols. From its inception around the middle of the seventeenth century, it was used well into the nineteenth when degenerate forms of these pistols were nothing more than costume accessories. While the ramshorn terminal is quite similar in all periods, the grip, which is very straight in early examples, during the eighteenth century gradually becomes curved to conform to current London trends.

Provenance: Herb Glass, 1967.
Overall length, 14½ in. (36.8 cm.); barrel, 8¾ in. (22.2 cm.); caliber, .62

---

[1] C. E. Whitelaw, "A Treatise on Scottish Hand Firearms of the XVIth, XVIIth & XVIIIth Centuries," in Herbert J. Jackson, *European Hand Firearms of the Sixteenth, Seventeenth & Eighteenth Centuries* (London, 1923), pl. VII, fig. 25.

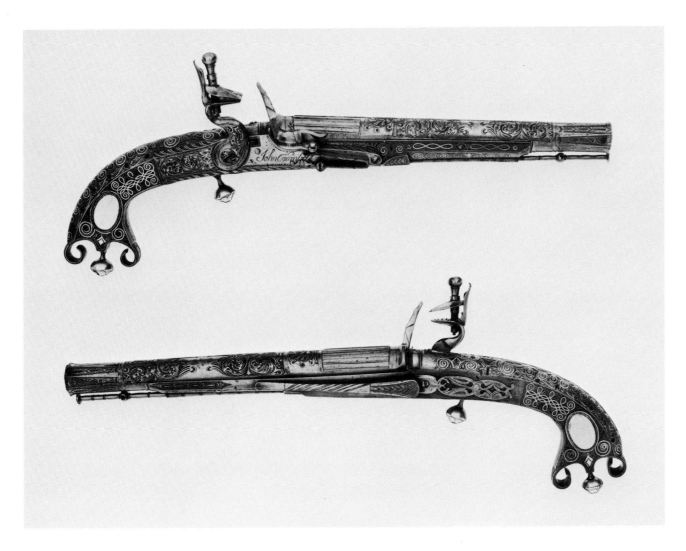
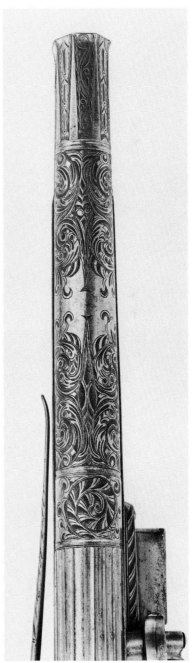

40 Flintlock Repeating Pistol

ENGLISH (LONDON), ca. 1800

THE walnut grip is relief carved with military trophies around the tang and is inlaid with silver wire and engraved sheet silver foliage. On either side of the grip are cast silver plaques gilded, pierced, and chased in vegetal designs. The twist barrel is octagonal and flares slightly at the breech and muzzle. It is blued and is overlaid with chased silver flowers and trophies; a riband on the two side flats is engraved with the inscription H.W. MORTIMER LONDON on the obverse, and on the reverse, GUNMAKER TO HIS MAJESTY. Its back-action flintlock has flat surfaces blued and overlaid with silver military trophies and leaf borders. Just forward of the cock, the hinged door of the priming magazine and the pivot screw of the loading drum are likewise decorated. On the reverse, the face of the drum and its loading lever have similar silver overlay. Behind the lever a hinged door gives access to the powder and ball magazine within the breech housing. The housing is signed H.W. MORTIMER LONDON directly below the lockplate and GUNMAKER TO HIS MAJESTY continues on the other side of the triggerguard. The silver buttcap and escutcheon are chased with military trophies and gilt.

H. W. Mortimer, who had his shop at 89 Fleet Street, London, was appointed gunmaker to King George III in 1783. After his death, his son, also H. W., with whom he had been in partnership, maintained the business at this address well into the nineteenth century.

This pistol is made in the Eastern or "Turkish taste," as is demonstrated by the character of much of its ornament. The firm of Mortimer is known primarily for the excellence of its pistols and double guns, which were produced in the severe taste of the latter part of the eighteenth century. This pistol, while atypical of their work, does conform to a contemporary fad for Eastern design both in England and on the Continent. Blair cites a contemporary London advertisement for English-made "TURKISH ORNAMENTS in the newest taste."[1] However, it must not be ruled out that it may also have been intended for Eastern presentation, since in 1801 the United States government commissioned eighteen firearms from Mortimer and Son, gold mounted and some with diamonds, for presentation to the Bey of Tunis,[2] which explains the statement, "Gunmaker . . . to the United States of America" on his later trade labels. The massive size and garish ornament of this pistol are common to arms made for the Eastern market. All attempts at oriental design are confined solely to military trophies, which are exotic adaptations of standard European neoclassical patterns. The quality of the silverwork varies considerably, the cast elements exemplifying the two extremes. The plaques applied to the sides of the grip are of the finest execution.

The repeating magazine system utilized on this pistol is of Italian origin and had been in vogue for well over a century prior to its use here. While it is popularly known as the Lorenzoni system, its inventor is unknown and opinion is divided as to whether the oldest examples are by Lorenzoni of Florence or Giacomo Berselli of Bologna. The English type is readily discernable from its Italian counterparts and dates

---

[1] Blair, *Pistols*, p. 105.
[2] Hayward, *Gunmaker*, II, p. 227.

back to at least the 1690s. It is characterized by a large metal housing that covers the underside of the stock to approximately the tail of the lockplate. To this is mounted the triggerguard, and on the reverse side is hinged the horizontal magazine access door. This door is rectangular in the lower portion covering the powder chamber, while a circular upper extension covers a like chamber for the balls. The earliest examples exhibiting these English features are several longarms signed by John Cookson. Citing the similarity between the faceted and fluted barrel of an Italian example signed Bartolomeo Cotel (Tower of London, No. XII-473) with at least two Cookson pieces, recent writers have suggested that Cookson may have marketed Italian actions under his own signature. However, this form of breech decoration origi-

nated in Paris in the 1660s, and was internationally popular by the time these arms were produced.

In view of the constructional features and the stocking and engraving—the latter corresponding to that on signed works by documented English makers—the Cookson arms must at this time be considered English. This Mortimer pistol, and the numerous other English examples of this system, are the direct descendents of the Cookson firearms.

Provenance: Comte de Nesselrode, Château de Tzarevtchina; Edward H. Litchfield, New York City; Joe Kindig, Jr., York, Pennsylvania.
Overall length, 19¾ in. (49.2 cm.); barrel, 10 in. (25.4 cm.); caliber, .63

40

THE boundaries of modern Germany have little bearing on the Germanic cultural areas of the sixteenth through the eighteenth centuries—the period covered by the firearms in this collection. These arms represent the production of gunmaking centers within Habsburg possessions like Prague and Vienna, and in Bavaria such as Munich, Augsburg, and Nuremberg.

Wheel-locks, appearing at the beginning of the sixteenth century, were the most popular system of ignition during the next hundred and fifty years. While probably not a German invention, the wheel-lock so dominated production there that it virtually excluded the adoption of any other system appearing during this period. In the second half of the seventeenth century, the wheel-lock persisted in spite of strong inroads made by the flintlock of French type, examples being found from as late as the second decade of the eighteenth century.

The majority of the earliest surviving wheel-locks are of German origin and come from the second quarter of the sixteenth century. They show the development of the cheekstock and its butt-trap which were, by mid-century, to become the standard features of the Germanic wheel-lock gun. The gun in this collection, No. 41, among the earliest of these arms, shows both features essentially as they will be found throughout the existence of the wheel-lock in Germany. The substantial number illustrated here—many dated—enables us to follow its subsequent development to the final years of the seventeenth century. We have traced here the evolution of the new stock form appearing toward the end of the sixteenth century and have introduced the term "Z stock" for its description (see No. 52).

With the supremacy of the flintlock, German arms begin to conform, although usually belatedly, to French fashion. Only a few exceptions such as Bongarde (No. 58) and Hess (No. 64) show a good awareness of prevailing Paris style.

57

41 *Wheel-lock Carbine*

GERMAN, ca. 1540

THE cherry stock is inlaid with engraved staghorn designs and is tipped with a staghorn cap. There is also a staghorn buttplate with a sliding horn panel covering a hole for the storage of several balls, and a ground ball (replaced, not seen in photographs). The sliding butt-trap cover has a gilt-bronze rosette forming the head of the latch. The parcel gilt iron triggerguard is faceted in a diamond pattern. A gilded belthook is attached to the stock opposite the lock. The octagonal barrel has gilded relief moldings at the extreme breech. It tapers to the muzzle where similar opposed moldings are followed by an acanthus leaf girdle and a flared section upon which the facets shift to an octagonal section forming a hog's back. An integral front sight is located on the upper angle just above the convex muzzle. A tubular balustrate rear sight is brazed to the breech. The blued lockplate is etched and engraved and has a gilded border. Its external wheel has an iron cover on which a sliding panel conceals a square hole cut in the end of the arbor to receive the spanner. An external safety is mounted at the rear of the lock. The trigger has a screw with which to adjust its tension. The brass tag on the forestock numbered W.882 has been identified by Dr. Arne Hoff as relating to the inventory of the collection of Wilhelmshöhe.

This carbine is one of the limited number of surviving wheel-locks belonging to the second quarter of the sixteenth century, and it has a number of features in common with the earliest datable examples. One of these is the long forward extension of the lockplate that completely backs the dog spring. The latter is made with a very short lower leaf by which it is attached to the plate. The dog has small jaws, the upper of which is movable, and is of the earliest straight-necked form. An apparently unique feature is the sliding panel on the wheel cover, which gives access to the normally awkwardly projecting wheel arbor. The shape of the butt-stock with its lack of bulk is also consistent with the assigned date. Its gently curved upper profile and the lightness of its cheekpiece, which does not overhang the butt as in later examples, is to be seen among the wheel-locks in the *Illuminated Inventory* of the Emperor Charles V (d. 1558) as are two examples of a similar butt-trap. This type of trap, which continues the contour of the stock, lacks the pronounced projection and contour that calls attention to it as a prominent element of the buttstock, unlike trap covers of the latter part of the century.

The restrained use of staghorn inlay on this piece is in direct contrast to the apparent *horror vacui* of gunsmiths who followed the Germanic tradition during the second half of the sixteenth century. This restraint may be due, in part, to the earliness of the piece. Certainly the arms in the *Illuminated Inventory* are remarkable for their simplicity. The battle scene depicted on the reverse of the stock apparently showing a pikeman dispatching a mounted Turk while another Turk flees on horseback is undoubtedly a vivid reference to the immediate Austro-Turkish conflict. Two exotic birds depicted in the inlay of the left forend are a pelican and what seems to be an American turkey. Both may have been known to the artist only through illustrations, but the turkey apparently was introduced into Europe during the third decade of the sixteenth century.

The serpentine triangular inlays flanking the tang are repeated in the inlay of the extreme forend and in the engraving of the flared muzzle section. These same engraved elements are combined to form a sunburst design on the wheel cover. Elongated triangular stock inlays and engraved patterns are frequently encountered on wheel-locks of Germanic origin. By employing the serpentine form, the maker has achieved greater artistic success than by utilizing the purely geometric triangles.

The nearest related example that we have found is a wheel-lock saddle gun dated 1531 (K.30) in the Real Armería in Madrid. The shape of its butt is somewhat more archaic, but the form, and particularly the engraved and gilded decoration of the lock, are closely associated. However, a very similar trigger construction[1] relates it to a wheel-lock carbine dated 1548 in the Tøjhusmuseet in Copenhagen (B35) and probably represents the earliest stage in the development of the set trigger.

Provenance: Sotheby (William G. Renwick Collection, Pt. I), July 17, 1972, lot 15.
Overall length, 37⅜ in. (95 cm.); barrel, 25⅞ in. (65.8 cm.); caliber, .50

---

[1] Hoff, *Feuerwaffen*, II, p. 87, gives a diagram of a virtually identical mechanism, while the gun itself is illustrated ibid., I, p. 56.

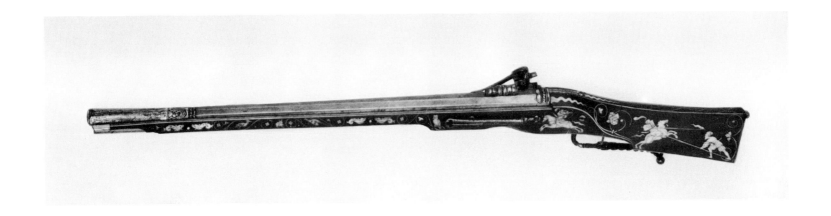

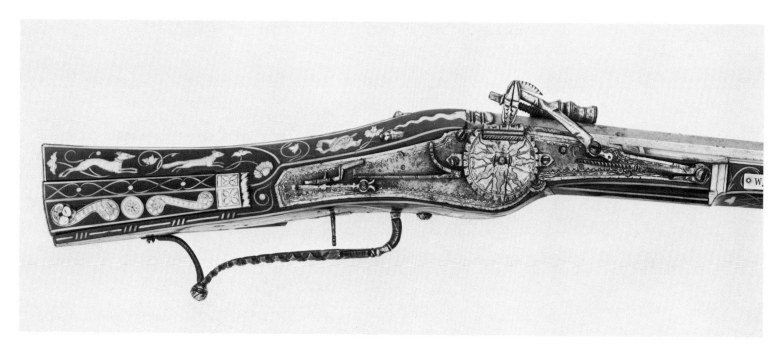

41

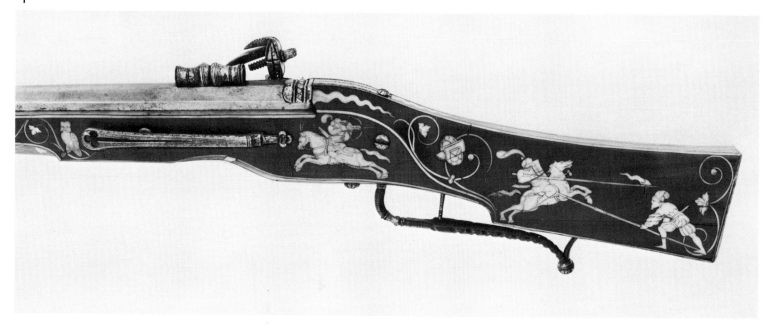

41

42 Pair of Wheel-lock Pistols

GERMAN (AUGSBURG?), ca. 1570

THE fruitwood stocks are inlaid on the sides with engraved ivory and staghorn hunting scenes and a castle. On the top of the grip are staghorn figures representing Adam, Eve, and the serpent, and just below these the initials V.M.L. A horn plaque carved with the low relief bust of a man in contemporary costume is on the back of the faceted pommel. The octagonal and round barrels have integral foresights at their extreme muzzle and are etched in geometrical patterns over their entire surface. A gilded ground highlights this etching at the breech, transition, and muzzle. Two falchion maker's stamps (Støckel 5812) are struck in the top flat of the breech. The locks are decorated with etched and engraved ornament, and originally both lockplate border and external wheel were gilded. An external safety is fitted at the rear of the plate and there is a pancover release button. The plain iron triggerguards are held by the tang screw.

The tentative attribution to Augsburg is based on the small scale of the pommel as well as on its decoration. The inlaid band around the midsection and the repeated lion masks holding rings are engraved flat representations of relief metal ornament often found on the pommels of Augsburg pistols. These stylistic features seem to support Støckel's suggestion that the falchion barrel marks were also used by an Augsburg smith.

Provenance: Sotheby (William G. Renwick Collection, Pt. IX), March 18, 1975, lot 49.
Overall length, 27 in. (68.6 cm.); barrel, 17⅞ in. (45.4 cm.); caliber, .49

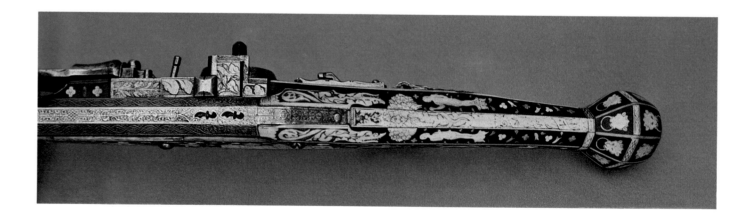

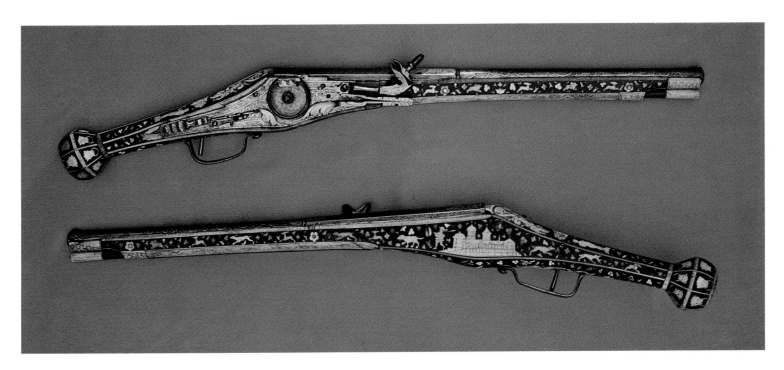

43 *Wheel-lock Gun*

SOUTH GERMAN, ca. 1570

THE full cherry stock is inlaid overall with engraved staghorn; interspersed small elements are dyed green. The butt-trap cover is made of engraved staghorn, and the butt ends in a staghorn plate. Among the engraved figures is a military procession of dogs and rabbits on the cheekpiece, and, on the underside, from butt to forend, figures framed in columned arches labeled MERCVRIVS, SPES, VENVS, GEOMETRIA. Unlabeled are a classical warrior and two female figures representing Lucretia and Fortune. On the side opposite the lock, Hercules is shown slaying the dragon Ladon in the Garden of the Hesperides. The blued barrel is damascened in silver and gold. Its octagonal breech approaches half its full length; there is no decorative transition to round. The muzzle is abruptly flared. The gilded rear peep sight has a removable copper insert, and the foresight is integral and gilded. The octagonal section has damascened arched panels in the general style of the decoration of the underside of the stock. The round forward section has a classical warrior in its center, the remainder is decorated with birds and flowers, and the whole is framed with a silver band. The blued lockplate and domed wheel cover are damascened in silver and gold. The dog, external safety, springs, pancover release, and wheel housing are gilded. The pancover and pan are modern replacements. The iron triggerguard is blued and the straight grip rail is damascened en suite with the lock and barrel.

The outstanding quality and style of this gun includes it among a small number of similar South German firearms from the third quarter of the sixteenth century. It exhibits the decorative vocabulary that dominated at this time and in this area. The style is characterized by stock decoration that includes a parade of framed allegorical and mythological figures, the labors of Hercules, pierced scrolls, and naturalistic and anthropomorphized animals. The metal decoration consists of isolated gilded areas—sometimes in chiseled and etched strapwork—seen here in damascened patterns in silver and gold against a blued ground. With its combination of polychromed stock and mounts, this gun achieves a decorative impact seldom equaled.

Provenance: William Randolph Hearst; Fischer Gallery, Lucerne, June 24, 1974, lot 85.
Overall length, 43¾₆ in. (110 cm.); barrel, 32⁵⁄₁₆ in. (82.7 cm.); caliber, .56

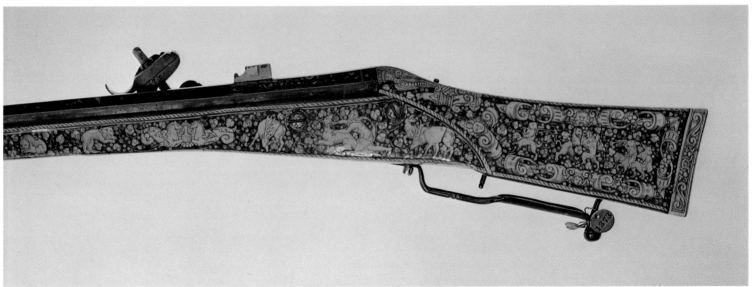

43

43

44 *Wheel-lock Pistol*

SOUTH GERMAN, *ca. 1580*

THE fruitwood stock is heavily inlaid with engraved stag-horn plaques and tendril volutes. Along the entire underside is a series of unlabeled allegorical and mythological figures in arched panels. The reverse contains scenes of an outdoor feast with figures in more contemporary dress; the obverse has running animals along the forend. The pommel is divided into panels containing classical portrait medallions and squirrels; the chamois engraved boss may be an old replacement. The inlay is missing from the top forward edges of the forend. The initials MI are engraved in the staghorn behind the barrel tang. The octagonal and round barrel makes its transition at the midpoint with a simple filed ring. The breech has a lightly engraved border at its extreme end and is struck with a partly defaced maker's mark (possibly Støckel 5136). The muzzle is slightly swelled. The plain lock has an external wheel with a domed cover and an external safety, while the iron triggerguard has a central turning.

This pistol belongs to the South German group discussed with the preceding gun (No. 43). The engraving of this example, while good, is not as fine as that of the gun. The stocker MI has used the squirrel excessively, unlike the stocker of the previous piece who emphasized the lion. The boss of the pommel is of inferior quality horn and the engraving of the chamois is strikingly similar to nineteenth-century German decoration. The overall impression given by this pistol is pleasing; the plainness of the lock and barrel emphasizes the stock inlay.

Provenance: Frank E. Bivens, Los Angeles, California, 1976.
Overall length, 22¼ in. (57 cm.); barrel, 13½ in. (34.5 cm.); caliber, .59

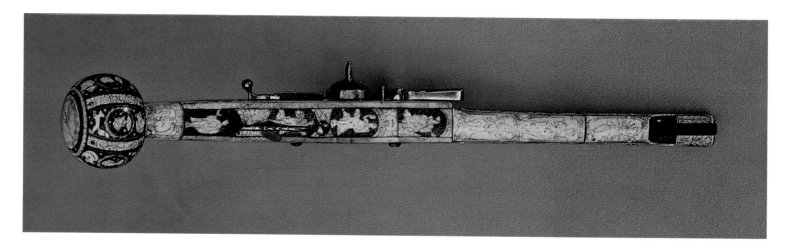

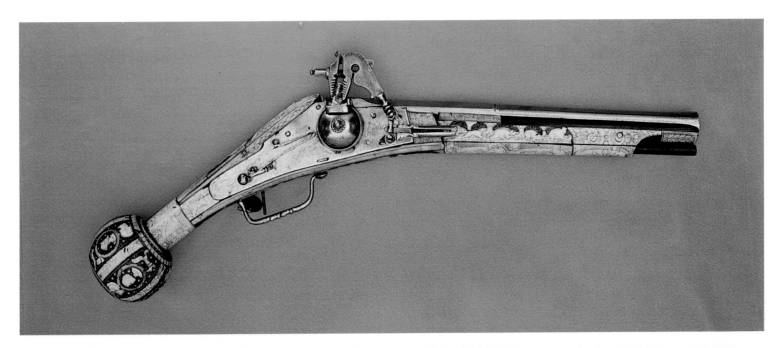

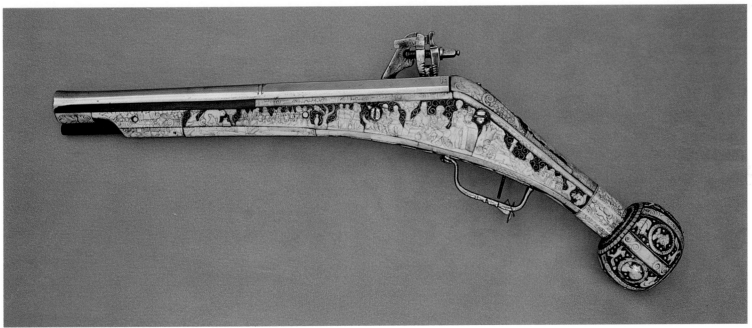

45 *Snap-matchlock Rifle*

GERMAN (NUREMBERG), dated 1581

ENGRAVED staghorn inlay covers the fruitwood full stock. The butt, of German cheekstock form, terminates in an iron ground ball; a wave molding is cut along the top edges of the forend the full length of the barrel. There is no provision for a ramrod. The stock is dated 1581 behind the trigger, and has the inlaid initials HD behind the barrel tang. The full octagonal barrel is tapered from the breech and flares again for its forward fifth, where it shifts one-sixteenth of a turn to produce a mid-ridge at the top to which is affixed the brass blade foresight. The large engraved rear sight is dovetailed to the extreme breech. Its sliding top permits the insertion of removable copper peepsight leaves. On the top flat forward of the sight is the stamped maker's mark HA; this is flanked by two Nuremberg control marks. The barrel is rifled with sixteen grooves. The tang screw is a modern replacement; the original traversed the stock vertically from forward of the trigger. The priming pan and manual pancover are screwed to the side of the barrel. The lock has a flat engraved plate and a serpentine with baluster turnings and is held to the stock by wood screws at its extremes. The set trigger is cocked by pulling the cord that passes through the plate.

This rifle belongs to a group of some twenty snap-matchlock rifles, a number of which bear dates in the 1580s and 1590s. In an article on this group, Dr. Arne Hoff has pointed out that the style of these rifles was archaic when they were manufactured in spite of the fact that the majority were luxury arms.[1] They are all rifled and have fine peep sights as well as a form of set trigger. They are not fitted with triggerguards, and their stocks have no provision for a ramrod. These features, as well as pictorial evidence, have led Dr. Hoff to conclude that these rifles were made for competitive match shooting. Their obvious opulence eliminates economy as an explanation for their archaic form and antiquated mechanism. Rules established by early shooting societies may have dictated this use of the matchlock thus creating this expensive novelty.

The artistic quality of this rifle places it among the finest of extant examples. In its marquetry it is closely related to a like rifle in the Wallace Collection, London, whose stock is dated 1598 (A. 1072) and to two undated rifles in the Musée de l'Armée, Paris (M.9 and M.24).

Provenance: Samuel J. Whawall; William Randolph Hearst; Stephen V. Grancsay, Brooklyn, New York.
Overall length, 50 in. (127 cm.); barrel, 38¾ in. (98.5 cm.); caliber, .69

---

[1] Arne Hoff, "Late Firearms with Snap Matchlock," *Tøjhusmuseets Skrifter*, VII (Copenhagen, 1963).

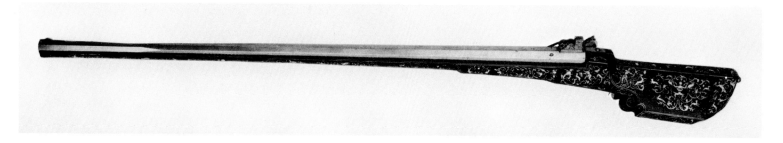

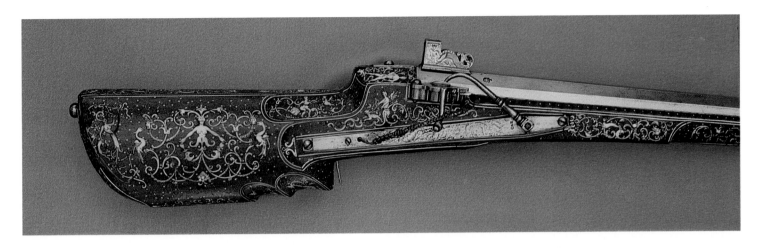

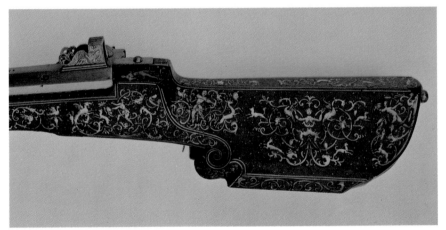

46 *Wheel-lock Pistol*

GERMAN (SAXON), dated 1586

THE fruitwood stock is heavily inlaid with fine staghorn floral scrolls bordered by engraved staghorn sheets. The blued octagonal and round barrel has course moldings filed at the breech that flank a swan maker's mark similar to Støckel 5943, but reversed. Just forward of the moldings are two stampings of the mark P. H. combined within a shield struck twice. The date 1586 is struck into the top flat. A band of stamped rosettes encircles the muzzle. The blued lock has an enclosed wheel, an external manual safety, and a pancover release button. A simple iron triggerguard is retained by the head of the tang screw. The wooden ramrod has an engraved staghorn tip.

This pistol is one of many of similar type sold from the Dresden Armories. It forms part of a large dated series that probably indicates its military purpose. While the great majority of these pistols are very plain (see No. 47), others such as this one display a profusion of fine quality stock inlay which may show that they were intended for special use.

Here the restriction of the full coverage of the stock inlay to the pommel end is unusual, but only this portion would have been visible when the pistol was carried in its saddle holster. Some other examples from the same source have this full coverage for their entire length. Another feature that seems to be common to all three categories of this group is the utilitarian aspect of the metal parts which, combined with the more ornate stocks, makes them strikingly incompatible.

The accompanying cartridge box is not known to be original to this pistol, but it has similar voluted inlay and probably comes from the same period and source. It contains four compartments for paper cartridges. Its iron cover and suspension loops were originally blued.

Provenance: Sotheby, March 23, 1970, lot 22.
Overall length, 21 in. (53.3 cm.); barrel, 13 in. (33 cm.); caliber, .58

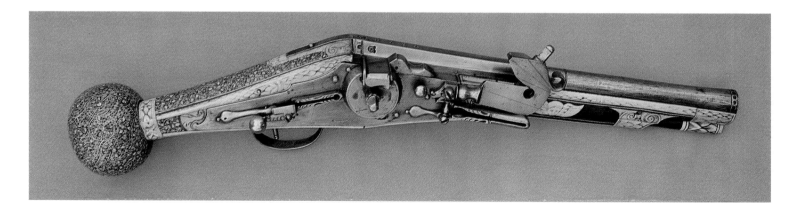

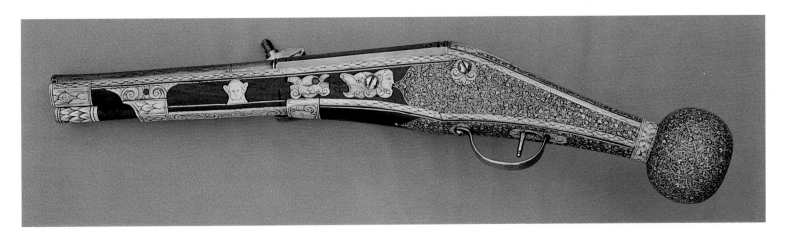

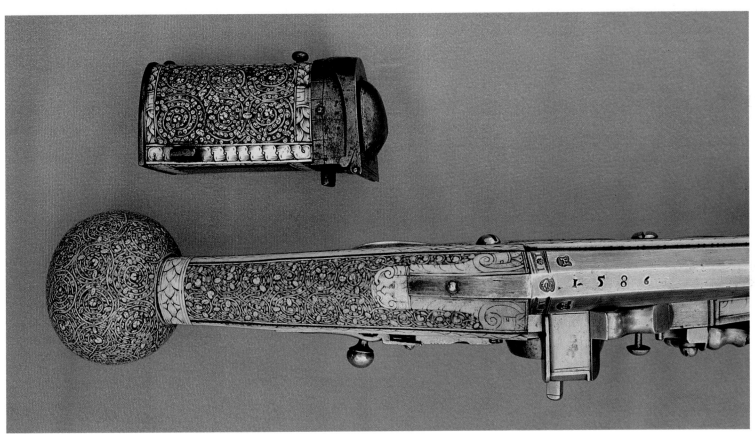

47 Pair of Wheel-lock Pistols

GERMAN (SAXON), dated 1588

THE blackened stocks have an impressed texture and engraved staghorn inlays; their ball pommels terminate in a round silver plaque engraved with a classical warrior's bust and floral scrolls. The blued octagonal barrels become round at approximately one-half their length; the muzzles are slightly flared. A few punched designs decorate the barrel flats. Struck in the breech is the barrel maker's mark (Støckel 3841) followed by the stamped date 1588. The blued locks have an enclosed wheel and external safety.

These pistols are part of a large series released from the Dresden Armories in sales over the past century. They are all virtually identical in design and workmanship, and are dated in the last decades of the sixteenth century. Many have the arms of Saxony engraved on the butt. The stocks' roughened surface offers a firmer grip for the hand, and it has been suggested that this artificial texturing may be a stylized representation of staghorn. The quality and large number of the arms indicate that they were made for military use; these pistols may be contrasted with the single pistol (No. 46) whose stock is much more elaborate but is otherwise of identical form. The latter, from the same source, may represent an officer's model from this series.

The contemporary accoutrements—spanner, priming flask, and cartridge box—are not known to have accompanied this pair, but are appropriately included with them because of their allied workmanship. The spanner has three apertures for arming the wheel and tightening the dog jaws onto the stone. The opposite end terminates in a screwdriver blade. The circular wooden priming flask is finished en suite with the gunstocks. Its round silver plaque is engraved in a combination of floral and geometric designs, and in its center is a small stamped mark that appears to be a griffon's head. A cartridge box, also en suite, is drilled to receive four paper cartridges. It is mounted in iron etched in floral designs. Below the hinge of the cover, which is inscribed NVMERI 31, is the date 1587.

Provenance: Prince Ernst Heinrich of Saxony, 1926; Bashford Dean; Stephen V. Grancsay, Brooklyn, New York.
Overall length, 22 in. (55.9 cm.); barrel, 13 in. (23 cm.); caliber, .68

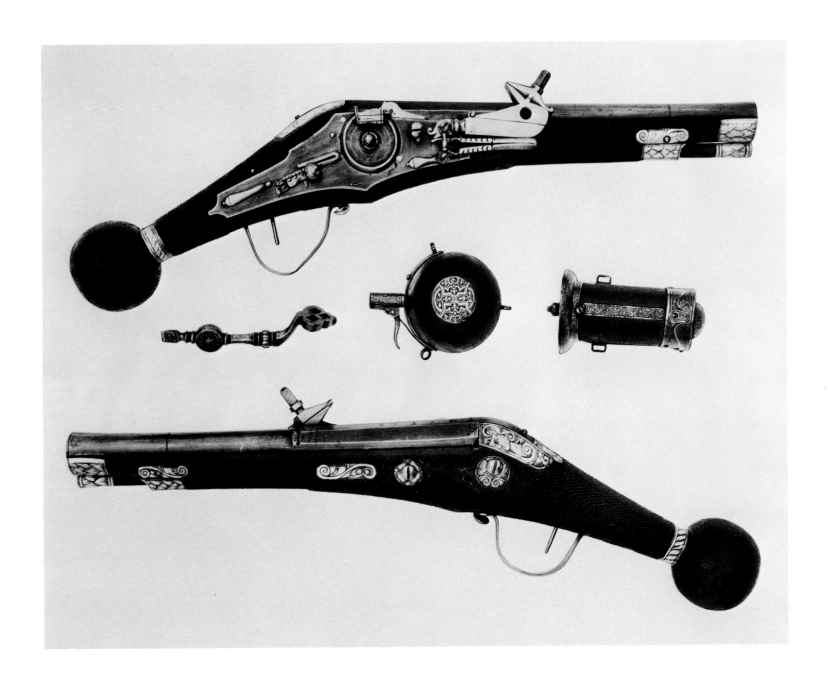

48 Double Wheel-lock Pistol

SOUTH GERMAN, ca. 1595

THE cherry stock is inlaid with borders, dots, and engraved plaques of staghorn. The plain octagonal and round barrel flares slightly at the muzzle. Two wheel-locks with opposing dogs are combined on a single plate. The externally mounted wheels have open partial covers and button pancover releases. The safety for the forward lock is centrally mounted between the wheels, while that for the rear is located on the reverse of the stock. There is a simple iron triggerguard and a baluster-turned trigger.

This pistol is designed to fire two charges superimposed from the same barrel. Two sears are activated by a single trigger, and firing can be controlled by the use of individual safeties. The diameter of the bore is reduced for the breech charge. The barrel and the general form of the stock relate this pistol to the preceding arms from the Dresden Armories series. The shape taken by the ball butt in this instance suggests an early stage in the evolution of the pear-shaped pommel.

Overall length, 18¾ in. (47.5 cm.); barrel, 12⅜ in. (31.5 cm.); caliber, .60

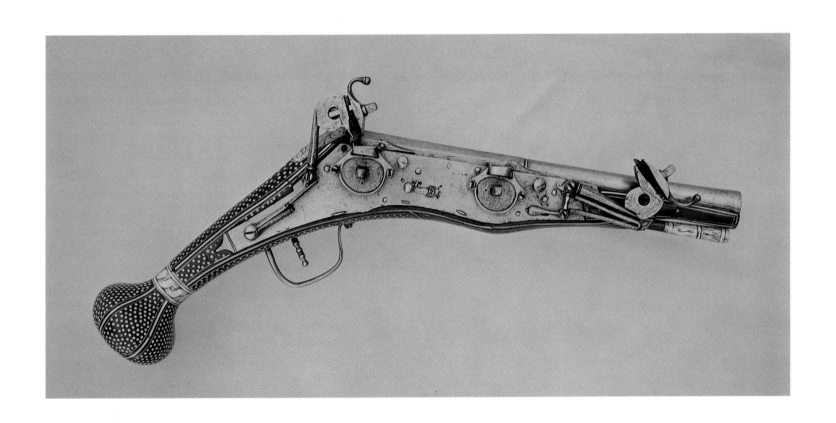

49 Double Wheel-lock Pistol

GERMAN (NUREMBERG), dated 1600

THE cherry stock has foliate designs, masks, and borders inlaid in engraved staghorn. Behind the barrel tang are engraved the initials ND. The barrel, designed to fire superimposed charges, has an octagonal breech slightly longer than the round forward section, which is formed in a hog's back along its upper portion in the manner of a sighting rib. Heavy turned moldings are at the breech, transition, and muzzle. The transition is further decorated with a chiseled acanthus leaf and gilding. The breech flats are engraved with longitudinal lines, and the uppermost is stamped with the Nuremberg control mark and the date 1600. The stamped maker's initials VK (similar to Støckel 4686) flank the Nuremberg mark. The lock has two external wheels fitted with convex, pierced, and engraved covers. The plate is engraved with a simple border, and the dog faces are engraved. Each wheel has an external safety and an individual pancover release. The combined initials VK (Støckel 4688) appear on the plate by the rear wheel. The trigger has balustrate turnings and terminates in an acorn, and the iron triggerguard has central turnings and a flattened and pierced rear section. The pommel, which retains a small pierced and contoured iron plate, has a turned iron finial.

During the 1590s radical changes were taking place in the design of German wheel-lock pistols. The abruptly angled grip gradually straightened and the previously spherical or slightly flattened ball butt became elongated. These changes resulted in a stock with a very straight grip, a noticeably elongated pommel of either pear or lemon form, and a profile that assumed the shape of a flattened Z. The evolution was complete by 1605 or 1610 (see No. 52). Dated 1600, this Nuremberg pistol was manufactured during this transitional period and is one of the earliest examples of the lemon pommel on a pistol whose precise date of manufacture is known. However, the stock form, although straighter than that of the previous double lock pistol (No. 48, ca. 1595), is evolving in the direction of the Z stock. While the double lock form may have hampered the fullest execution of the Z stock, the trend toward the straight stock is obvious here. The origin of this development is obscure and is fully discussed with the above mentioned 1610 pistol.

The accessories shown include a wooden powder flask, inlaid in a manner similar to the pistol stock, with the engraved initials IC in its center. The spanner, of typical German form, has a priming flask in its shaft which terminates in a screwdriver.

Provenance: Frank E. Bivens, Los Angeles, California, 1976.
Overall length, 20⁷⁄₁₆ in. (52 cm.); barrel, 11⅝ in. (29.5 cm.); caliber, .52

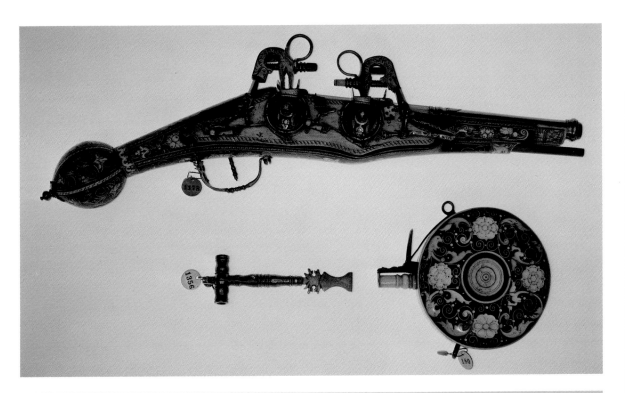

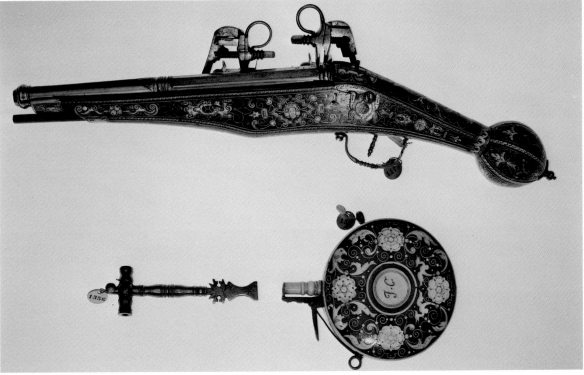

50 *Wheel-lock Pistol with Left-hand Lock*

SOUTH GERMAN (DRESDEN?), ca. 1600

THE fruitwood stock is inlaid with engraved staghorn plaques and borders. The plain octagonal and round barrel is slightly flared at the muzzle. The unusual left-hand wheel-lock has a covered wheel and a pancover release; the external safety is mounted on the reverse side of the stock. There is a simple iron triggerguard. The wooden ramrod has an engraved ivory tip.

While closely related to the preceding examples, this pistol displays another shape of buttstock that apparently is derived from forms used in Germany during the first half of the sixteenth century. The barrel form and the engraved stock ornament are very similar to those of arms coming from the Dresden Armories. This pistol seems to represent a transition from the sharply angled stock to the flattened Z style previously described.

Provenance: F. Theodore Dexter, Pasadena, California; Frank E. Bivens, Los Angeles, California, 1975.
Overall length, 20½ in. (52 cm.); barrel, 12⅞ in. (32.7 cm.); caliber, .52

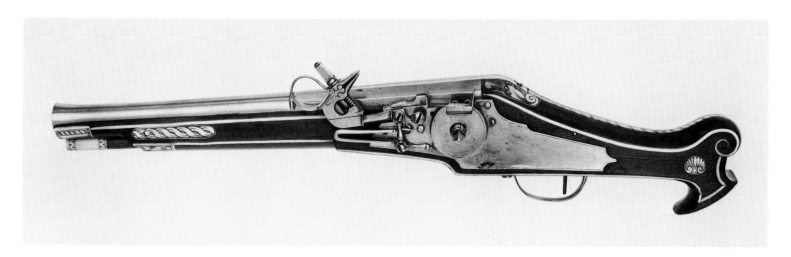

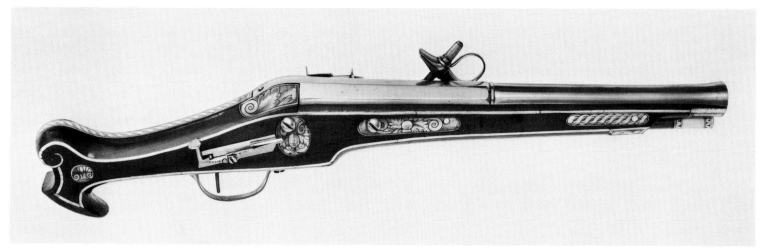

51 *Wheel-lock Pistol*

GERMAN (NUREMBERG), ca. 1605

THE ebony stock is inlaid with engraved staghorn and mother-of-pearl. The octagonal breech has raised gilded moldings and continues approximately one-third of the total barrel length, where its transition to round is achieved by a ring girdle. Etched panels with a gilded background decorate the breech, transition, and the area behind the ring-turned muzzle. The mark of Lorenz Herold (Støckel 529) is struck in the upper breech under the letters N over R (Støckel 1604), possibly the Nuremberg control. Forward of the breech etching are the faint remains of an inscription or a number. The lock has a gilded open wheel cover and a gilded pancover release in the form of a screw. The plate has an etched border with a gilded ground and is struck with the Nuremberg mark and the maker's mark (Støckel 3063), a shield containing a sunburst surmounted by the initials H.R. An external safety with a gilded lever is on the reverse of the stock. The lemon-shaped pommel is divided into five panels by gilt-bronze straps. The iron triggerguard and turned trigger are also gilded.

The date given to this pistol is somewhat earlier than that of the Dresden pair dated 1610 (No. 52), since it appears to have a slightly less developed form of the Z-shaped stock. The grip is more angled than on later examples, and the keel is only suggested by an inlay. As is not infrequently the case, the barrel marks on this pistol were struck in the breech subsequent to its etching, thereby carrying portions of the pattern into their recess and confusing their legibility. A double-barreled pistol with locks bearing this lockmaker's mark is illustrated and discussed in the Wallace Collection Catalogue.[1]

The accompanying ebony powder flask is not associated with the pistol, but its engraved staghorn moldings and mother-of-pearl inlays are compatible. It is fitted with engraved brass mounts that were originally gilded. The spout also serves as a powder measure.

Provenance: Joe Kindig, Jr., York, Pennsylvania, 1964.
Overall length, 31 in. (78.7 cm.); barrel, 22¾ in. (57.7 cm.); caliber, .35

---

[1] Wallace Collection Catalogues, *European Arms and Armour*, ed. Sir James Mann. II: *Arms* (London: Printed for the Trustees by William Clowes and Sons, Ltd., 1962), no. A1151 and pl. 189.

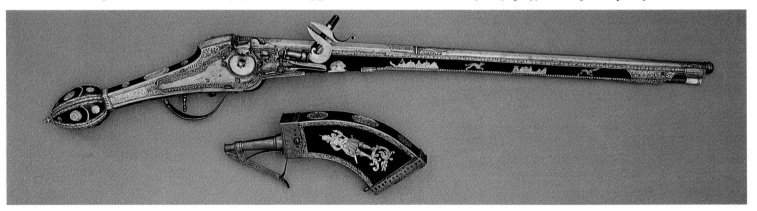

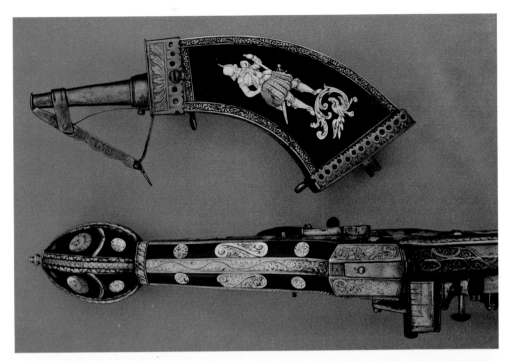

52 *Pair of Wheel-lock Pistols*

GERMAN (DRESDEN), dated 1610

THE full fruitwood stocks are inlaid with engraved staghorn. Plaques on either side of the barrel tang have the arms of Saxony and the Arch Marshalship of the Holy Roman Empire. The initials IZ are engraved directly behind the tang. The barrels have a short octagonal section at the breech, set off by beaded moldings enclosing simple punched designs. The maker's stamped initials SH (Simon Helbig of Dresden, Støckel 494) flank his stamp (Støckel 492), just forward of which is the stamped date 1610. The middle barrel section begins octagonal and gradually divides into raised pointed segments that enclose rounded areas. This creates a gradual transition to the round forward section where the barrel flares slightly and terminates in a convex muzzle turning. The wheel-locks are plain with the exception of engraved dogs. The wheel covers are convex and are attached to the plate by two screws. There is a pan-release button, and the trigger spring is attached to a simple iron triggerguard.

These pistols are typical of a series coming from the Dresden Armories, the same source as the previous pistols (Nos. 46 and 47). With their straight grip almost paralleling the axis of the barrel, they exhibit a reemphasis of a mid-sixteenth-century style. However, the addition of the pear-shaped pommel represents a modern departure from the ball butt, as does the introduction on pistol stocks of the abrupt step-down in the stock profile immediately behind the barrel tang. The latter feature, which seems to make more sense in the design of the rifle, occurs almost simultaneously about the turn of the century in both long and short arms. Balance is then maintained by the addition of a similar abrupt offset beneath the lock just forward of the triggerguard attachment, causing the stock profile to assume the shape of a flattened Z. In order to lighten its appearance, the lower offset may be coved toward the center, producing a mid-ridge or keel. This new stock form consequently caused a reshaping of the lock profile. In the Dresden series the earliest tendencies toward these new features occurs on pieces dated in the mid-1590s with the introduction of the faceted elongated pommel. These characteristics of the Dresden series seem to reflect like development in both Saxony and Bavaria. The origin of these new features is difficult to determine since similar developments occur in France and elsewhere at about the same time.

Provenance: Royal Gewehrkammer, Johannaeum, Dresden; Bashford Dean; George Terry.
Overall length, 29 in. (75 cm.); barrel, 18¾ in. (47.5 cm.); caliber, .58

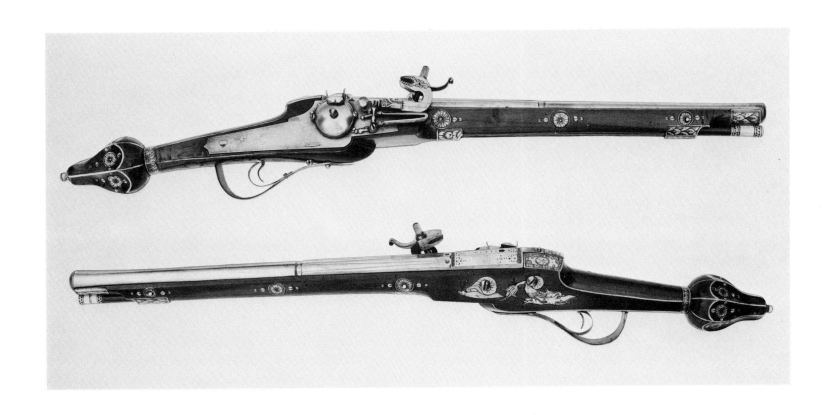

53 *Wheel-lock Pistol*

GERMAN (MUNICH), ca. 1630

THE plain ebony stock has relief molding around the barrel tang and fluted molding along the forend. The blued barrel is round with turned and octagonal moldings at the breech. The breech third of the barrel is relief chiseled with a gold damascened ground, and the forward two-thirds has four longitudinal raised ribs extending to the muzzle where there is a brass blade sight (probably replaced). A narrow panel along either side of the barrel adjacent to the edge of the stock is gilded. The blued lock has an external wheel that is totally covered by a separate wheel cover. It is decorated with relief-chiseled figures against a damascened ground. The pancover and columnar section of the sculptured dog are gilded. The mounts are of chiseled iron en suite with the lock and barrel. The inside of the triggerguard bow and its rear extension are gilded, while the outer sculptured portion of the bow is damascened. The forward ramrod pipe is a replacement, as is the horn forend cap. Two rosettes of mother-of-pearl serve as washers for the two gilded lock retaining screws.

In both design and execution this pistol represents the superb workmanship achieved by the school of ironworkers employed at the Munich court, which began in 1594 with the appointment of Emmanuel Sadeler of Antwerp as ironworker to the Duke of Bavaria. Upon Emmanuel's death in 1610 his brother Daniel received the appointment. Daniel in turn was succeeded in 1632 by Caspar Spät, possibly his disciple. Spät's death in 1691 brought to a close almost a century of adherence to a renaissance style introduced late in the sixteenth century by Emmanuel.

There is strong evidence to indicate that Antwerp was the source of the design of the chiseled elements so peculiar to the Munich school. Both Emmanuel and Daniel were apprenticed in Antwerp to their father, and later, after accepting positions in Munich and Prague respectively, continued working in virtually identical styles. When Daniel was induced to come to Munich to succeed his brother in 1611, there was no break in the continuity of design and execution established there by Emmanuel. In fact, this situation continued until late in the century with the death of Spät. What had become by then an archaic renaissance style may be traced back to late sixteenth-century patterns produced by Antwerp designers. It should be noted, moreover, that these iron chiselers of the Munich school were not gunsmiths. The Sadeler brothers had apparently trained as sword cutlers and decorators under their father. As ironworkers to the Munich court, they also decorated a variety of items not related to firearms. The most outstanding characteristic of the Munich style, originating with the Sadelers, is the boldly sculptured blued steel against a stippled gold ground.

This pistol shows the interesting adaptation of new flintlock forms in use in Western Europe during the 1630s and 1640s combined with traditional Munich design. The form of the triggerguard, barrel tang, and pommel cap is quite contemporary. The recurved bow of the guard attaches immediately forward of the trigger rather than to the bulge of the stock in the wheel-lock manner. Also characteristic of the flintlock guard is its attachment at the forward end by a transverse pin and its narrow rail held by a screw at the rear extreme. The absence of a lobate finial represents the earliest stage in the development of this type of guard. The pointed tang is an exaggeration of the truncated tapered form increasingly popular at this time, while the flat-sided pommel, oval in section, is also quite modern. Contrasting with these up-to-date features is the protective fitting on the forend at the ramrod's point of entry. This reproduces in iron the traditional staghorn fitting so characteristic of Germanic wheel-locks at a time when the flintlock was devoid of a rear thimble.

Quite similar to this piece is a pair of pistols in the Royal Armory at Turin (Nos. N. 27–28. See Blair, *Pistols*, pls. 42–43), which can be identified as coming from the workshop of Caspar Spät. These however lack the vigor in the quality of the steel chiseling and clarity of design of the present pistol, which may well represent one of the final products of the Daniel Sadeler period.

Provenance: Edward H. Litchfield, New York City; Joe Kindig, Jr., York, Pennsylvania; Arthur Yates, Costa Mesa, California. Overall length, 22½ in. (57.2 cm.); barrel, 14⅞ in. (37.7 cm.); caliber, .48

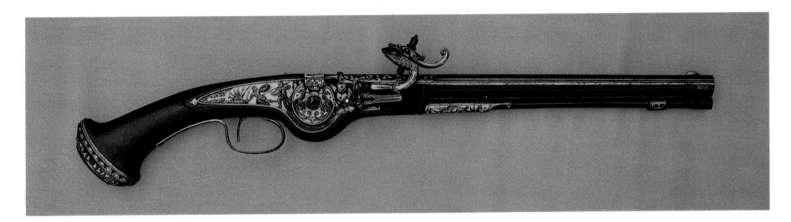

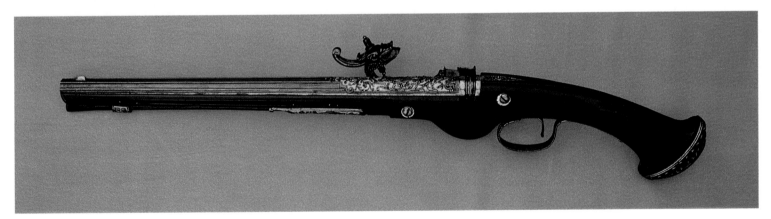

53

53

54 *Wheel-lock Pistol*

GERMAN (ARZBERG), ca. 1640

THE full fruitwood stock is darkened in coarsely carved areas. This is further enhanced by decorative iron nail-head studs. The forward half of the forend has been replaced. The barrel is octagonal at the breech where it is engraved, and gradually turns to round for the final three-quarters of its length. The wheel-lock mechanism is entirely enclosed. The convex lockplate is covered with cursory engraving in simple scroll and floral designs. On the reverse of the stock is a round cover that is hinged to give the spanner access to the wheel arbor. A button safety is located directly behind the iron trigger-guard.

This pistol is attributed to Georg Gsell on the basis of its lock form and decoration and the decoration of its stock. Identical engraving and stock decoration can be seen on a fully signed and dated (1649) wheel-lock rifle in the Vienna Waffensammlung (D. 291). A pair of pistols very similar to this example, also with enclosed wheel-locks, but signed by Jakob Gsell of Arzberg and dated 1652, are in the Hermitage Museum, Leningrad (No. 611). Støckel lists four gunmakers of the Gsell family working in Arzberg at approximately this time.

The decoration of this pistol is typical of that of arms by Gsell. Both the engraving and the stock carving are extraordinarily naive. The novelty of the pistol lies in the wheel-lock with its unusual internal mechanism. While unusual, this construction was known during the latter part of the sixteenth century and endured until the first quarter of the eighteenth. It is to be found on arms from Scandinavia, Germany, and Italy.

Provenance: Sotheby (Dagobert Runes Collection), June 11, 1964, lot 33.
Overall length, 25¼ in. (64 cm.); barrel, 28⅛ in. (46 cm.); caliber, .56

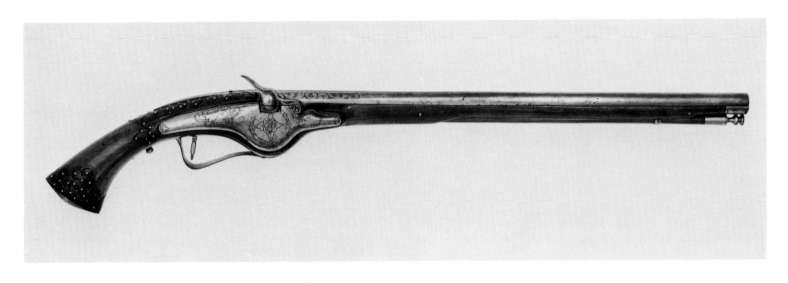

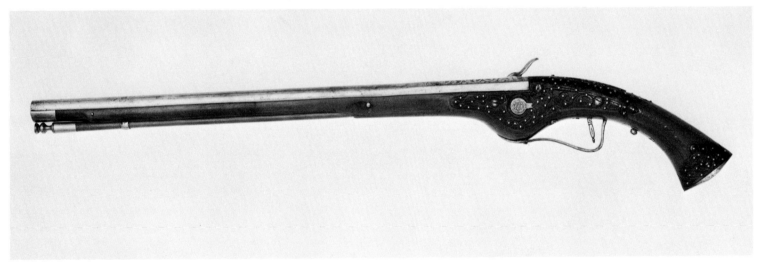

55 *Pair of Flintlock Pistols*

SWISS (ZURICH), ca. 1655

THE plain full stocks are of ebonized fruitwood. The gilt brass barrels are octagonal turning to sixteen-sided for two-fifths of the breech and then become round for the remainder following a small turning at the transition.

The flintlocks with flat surfaces and internal battery spring are entirely of gilt brass excepting the inner mechanism, screws, and battery face. The lock is engraved with grotesques and a hunting scene, and the plate terminates in a profiled animal's head. The triggerguards are of undecorated gilt brass. The gilt brass buttcaps are cast and chased in the design of the Austrian *Binnenschild*. The forend cap, ramrod pipe, and ramrod tip are of gilt brass decorated with die-stamped relief designs.

The Zurich gunsmith and goldsmith Felix Werder (1591–1673), to whom these pistols are attributed, was celebrated in his day for having developed a system for making pistol barrels entirely of brass with walls one-tenth as thin as those of ordinary cast barrels. His secret process or "invention," which first appears on a wheel-lock pistol bearing his name and the date 1640, was offered to the Royal Society at London in 1662

for the sum of two hundred doubloons. An article by Dr. Arne Hoff gives the results of his extensive investigation into the composition and construction of Werder's barrels.[1]

These pistols are certainly a tour de force of Werder's work, since he has constructed the lock almost entirely of brass including the cock and battery. Considering the stress that these parts must bear, they give equal testimony with the barrels to his brass hardening process.

The date assigned to these pistols was arrived at by comparing them to dated Werder pieces that consistently appear to lag some fifteen to twenty years behind their stylistic counterparts in Paris. These pistols rely for their decorative impact on their gilded metalwork contrasted with their ebonized stocks, and while the engraving is not of the quality one expects for this style, it does not detract from the overall impression (see Nos. 6 and 8).

Overall length, 22½ in. (57 cm.); barrel, 15¼ in. (38.7 cm.); caliber, .55

---

[1] Arne Hoff, "The Significance of 'Inventor' in Felix Werder's Signature," in Robert Held, ed., *Arms and Armor Annual*, I (Chicago: Follett Publishing Co., 1973), pp. 162–169.

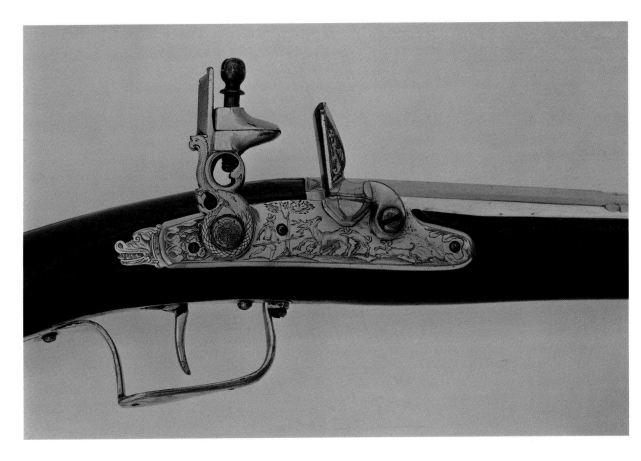

56 *Wheel-lock Rifle*

AUSTRIAN, ca. 1670

THE full ebonized fruitwood stock has relief-carved panels enclosed within inlaid borders contrasted with inlaid panels of engraved staghorn and mother-of-pearl. On the underside of the cheekpiece is the carved inscription N:10 and a secondarily carved crude 8. The sliding wood butt-trap cover is carved and inlaid en suite with the stock. A paper label on its inner face bears an illegible abbreviation and the number 13 in brown ink. The fire-blued octagonal barrel, rifled with six grooves, is tapered and flared and is lightly engraved at the breech and muzzle. The chiseled, blued, and gilded fixed rear sight has two folding leaves; the foresight is a silver blade. The unidentified brass maker's mark, a squirrel surmounted by the initials KZ within a shield, is stamped in the upper flat midway between the rear sight and the tang. The polished wheel-lock has flat surfaces and an enclosed wheel. Its pan and pancover are blued and gilded, and it is chiseled and engraved overall. The plate of the double-set triggers and the rear trigger are relief chiseled and engraved. The triggerguard, decorated en suite with the lock, is attached by the tang screw from above and two wood screws through its divided rear finial. A spirally fluted iron ground ball protects the staghorn buttplate.

This rifle, together with some fifty related firearms, is discussed by Professor Hans Schedelmann in his article, "The Master of the Animal-Head Scroll."[1] The author has pointed out that nearly all of these arms come from the second quarter of the seventeenth century and has speculated that they represent the work of a single stocker in Vienna.

While the design and execution of these arms show a close affinity, they could easily represent a school rather than the work of a single artisan. Typical of this group are the recessed panels with interlaced relief scrollwork featuring animal-head terminals and the scale carving of the underside of the buttstock. These scales, each of which is stamped with a dot or bead, may result from the influence of the Sadeler-Spät workshop of Munich. However, in the Munich school they were executed in chiseled iron with a central gold bead (see No. 53). While the carving of these stocks is ambitious in design and superb in quality, it displays a naiveté reminiscent of folk art. The ornament of the lockplate is in the style of Philippe Cordier, first published in France in 1635. The triggerguard is decorated en suite, but the configuration of the post and front extension comes from the Thuraine and le Hollandois flintlock style, as does the design of the inlaid staghorn border adjacent to the buttplate, thereby providing a date of ca. 1670. Consequently, this rifle is the latest known example of the animal-head scroll series.

Provenance: Collection Prince Thun, Teschen; William Randolph Hearst; Fischer Gallery, Lucerne, June 24, 1963, lot 136.
Overall length, 44 in. (112 cm.); barrel, 33½ in. (85.1 cm.)

---

[1] Hans Schedelmann, "The Master of the Animal-Head Scroll," in Robert Held, ed., *Arms and Armor Annual*, I (Chicago: Follett Publishing Co., 1973), pp. 180–195.

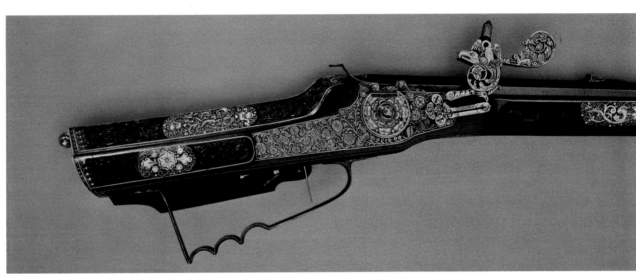

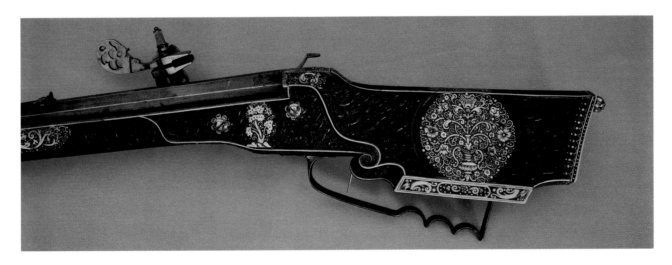

57 *Wheel-lock Rifle*

GERMAN (LANDSHUT), dated(?) 1695

THE full cherry cheekstock is heavily inlaid with engraved staghorn in both naturalistic and fanciful designs. The central figure in the hunting scene on the cheekpiece rides a horse on whose saddle blanket appears the crowned cipher C. The buttplate engraving includes the signature SAMVEL KLVGE · LANDSHVT on a riband. The release for the spring-activated butt-trap cover is concealed in the ornament under the stock. Engraved in the bottom of the butt-trap cavity is the inscription .W.S.95; the inner face of the cover has the carved number 13. The tapered and flared full octagonal barrel is engraved at the breech and has its original bright finish. The blued iron leaf rear sight has decorative balustrate finials at its front and rear; the brass blade foresight is slightly ogee in profile. The circular brass-lined maker's mark, HF over a bird, is stamped in the upper breech flat; a stamped X is at the rear of the left flat. The barrel is rifled with nine grooves. The lock with internal wheel is blued overall and its outer surface is overlaid with a heavy gilt-brass plaque pierced and engraved en suite with the stock, including the same mounted figure. The plaque is retained by gilt-brass screws from within. The pancover release button is recessed in the same manner as the butt-trap release; it is also brass-covered and engraved with a mask. Double-set triggers have a central adjustment screw; the blued plate terminates at the rear in a bulbous balustrate finial. The blued iron triggerguard has three finger rests on the grip rail and terminates at both ends in similar finials, the rear one of which is engraved with the number 13. The stock ends in a plain iron ground ball.

On this firearm are the signature and initials of what appear to be three craftsmen, none of whom is documented. The full signature of the probable engraver of the stock inlay, Samuel Kluge, also provides us with the place of manufacture. The incised initials W.S. in the butt-trap in conjunction with the numerals 95 may indicate the stocker and the date. Such a date would be consistent with the style of the gun. The crowned opposed C initials appearing on the saddle blanket may indicate that the mounted figure represents the owner of the arm. A most likely candidate is King Charles XI of Sweden (1655–1697), an avid gun collector and recipient of many gifts of arms, or possibly his contemporary, King Christian V of Denmark, who died in a hunting accident in 1699.

The superb quality of this arm is testimony to the entrenched wheel-lock tradition in Germany at a time when various versions of the snap flintlock had completely replaced it elsewhere in Europe. This form of cheekstock with its engraved horn decoration had persisted for well over a century and one-half by the time the arm illustrated was made. An early example is No. 41 in this collection. One hundred and fifty years later, the only concession to the flintlock influence on this Landshut rifle is the design of the triggerguard finials, which derive from French and Dutch arms of the 1660s.

Provenance: Rothschild Collection; Fischer Gallery, Lucerne, June 24, 1974, lot 91; Frank E. Bivens, Los Angeles, California, 1976.
Overall length, 50 1/16 in. (127.3 cm.); barrel, 38 in. (96.6 cm.); caliber, .51

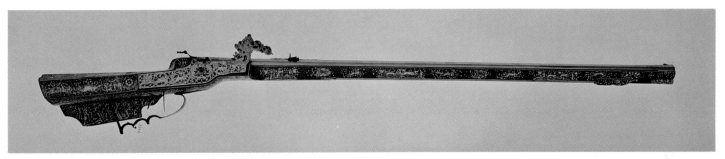

58 Pair of Flintlock Pistols

GERMAN (DÜSSELDORF), ca. 1695

THE full burl maple stocks have carving and borders in relief. The round barrels have three short relief panels along the breech with the uppermost panel and its flanking areas engraved. Relief chiseling covers the area between these and the raised sighting rib. The rib is engraved on both pistols with the signature BONGARDE DUSSELDORP. Convex lock surfaces are engraved and chiseled in relief, and the signature BONGARDE DUSSELDORP is repeated behind the cock. All iron mounts are relief chiseled except the bulbous turned forward thimble. The sideplate, escutcheon, triggerguard, and trigger are pierced.

Armand (Hermann?) Bongarde, who worked in Düsseldorf from at least 1678 until he died in 1727, was born in Süchteln only some thirty kilometers distant. Bongarde was perhaps the one foreign gunsmith working in the classical Louis XIV style whose work approaches that of the great Paris smiths in quality and design. He was appointed gunsmith in 1690 to the Elector Johann Wilhelm of Pfalz-Zweibrüken, for whom he had already made a superb garniture for the Electoral art collection. Zacharias von Uffenbach, who visited the residence early in the eighteenth century, was forced to don gloves before admiring the "incomparably chiseled and gilt" fowling piece, pistols, and sword by Bongarde.

Bongarde's arms on the whole adhere so intimately to Parisian fashion that the possibility exists that he may have trained in Paris. In any event, it is evident that he was familiar not only with contemporary pattern books, but with earlier French designs dating back to the middle of the century.

These pistols, in fact, show the strong influence of the Thuraine and le Hollandois style, which here has been so successfully interpreted in the Louis XIV manner that it may escape first examination.

The initial impression one receives from these pistols is that they belong to the 1680s, but closer study reveals details derived from patterns published by the Simonins in 1693, and even later unpublished elements from Piraube arms. Specifically, the pierced acanthus leaf triggerguard finial comes from pl. 9 of the Simonin book, while the escutcheon emulates that of the 1697 Piraube pistol illustrated here (No. 12). Many other obvious concepts standard to the classical Louis XIV style are shared by these pistols, the Simonin pattern book, and Piraube arms.

The grotesque masks used by Bongarde make an interesting study. On the sides of the pommels they follow the style of Thuraine and le Hollandois as well as that of Bérain's book in being composed almost entirely of foliage, unlike the more naturalistic masks of the Louis XIV style. Showing a related design approach, but less foliate, is the unusual combination of masks on the triggerguard with the Diana on the barrel, which may be peculiar to Bongarde himself. The mask on the triggerguard finial whose gaping mouth is formed by two opposing scrolls is more than suggestive of a like mask on pl. 11 of Jacquinet's engravings of designs by Thuraine and le Hollandois (1660). The reappearance of this design in de la Collombe's 1705 pattern book represents a revival of mid-seventeenth-century style, while its appearance on the Bongarde pistols ca. 1695 must be regarded as much a survival as the triggers with their pierced backplates. Certainly supporting this continuation of style are the hunched grotesque figures flanking the central medallion of the sideplate. Their origin appears to be the sideplate shown on pl. 7 of Jacquinet's album.

The superb quality of these pistols is evident not only in their execution but in their unity of design and the attention to small details. The iron chiseling is orderly in its distribution and avoids the clutter often seen in deluxe arms. This is continued into the stock carving to which it is closely related in theme and execution. The successful inclusion of the two lock screw heads within the design of the sideplate shows a rarity of concept not even presented by contemporary published patterns.

Provenance: Charles H. Moses, Ashtabula, Ohio, 1966.
Overall length, 21½ in. (54.5 cm.); barrel, 14⅞ in. (37.8 cm.); caliber, .66

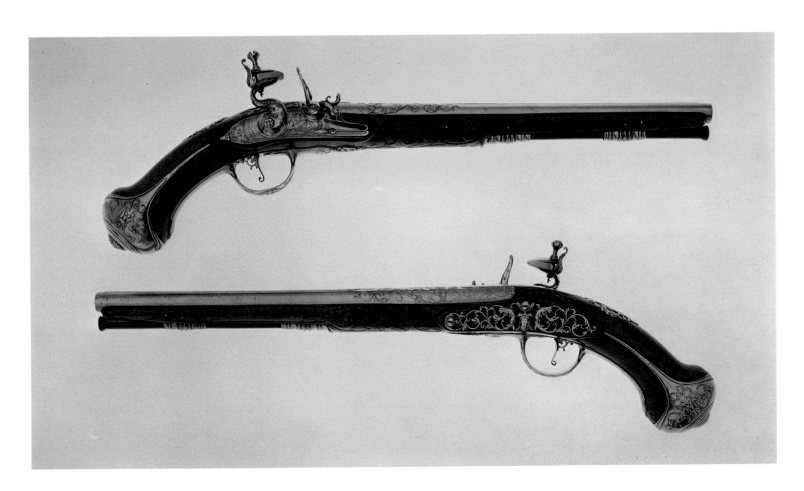

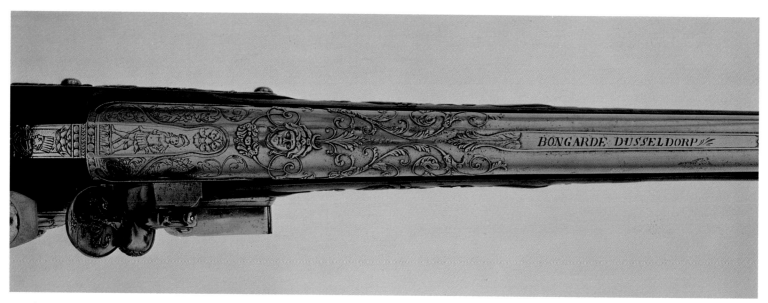

58

58

59 *Flintlock Wender Gun*

BOHEMIAN (PRAGUE), ca. 1700

THE full stump walnut stock is in two parts with relief moldings and floral scrolls. The round barrels have side flats along approximately one-quarter of their length extending forward from a heavily molded breech. The touch holes are gold lined. The breech section of the interrupted sighting rib on both barrels is inscribed JOHAN STIFFTER PRAG; the forward carries the elongated silver front sight. Trophies of arms are engraved on the round area of the breech. The convex lock surfaces are engraved on the plate and are chiseled in relief on the cock and both batteries. PRAG is inscribed on the plate behind the cock and I. STIFTER beneath both pans. A bas relief acanthus leaf frieze covers both segments of the swivel mechanism, which is released by the trigger when the lock is at half-cock. Mounts are of iron with the sideplate and escutcheon fully chiseled; the tang of the buttplate is in the form of a serpent in relief. There are three baluster-turned ramrod pipes.

It is probable that the Johan (Hans) Stifter who signed this piece belongs to the two generations of Hans Stifters working about this time in Prague. Their mark as recorded by Støckel is not to be found on this piece, but it is not consistently used on all Stifter arms.

This gun exemplifies the wide dissemination of Parisian style as reflected in Simonin's 1685 pattern book. In fact, pl. 8 supplied the central figures for the combat scene engraved on the lockplate,[1] while the chiseling of the cock and elements of the sideplate come from the lock on pl. 2.

The central grotesque heads of the sideplate repeat the concept depicted by the inlay to the rear of the safety of a much earlier wheel-lock pistol (No. 51) in this collection. However, its latest detail is the series of ring moldings at the extreme breech of the barrels that appear on Paris arms from the late 1690s. This piece shows an interesting departure from the standard shape of the Wender mechanism, which here is perfectly oval in section.

Provenance: John Hayward, London.
Overall length, 57¼ in. (145.5 cm.); barrel, 41⅞ in. (106.3 cm.); caliber, .57

---

[1] A pirated edition of pl. 8 is represented as pl. 2 (p. 73) and a pirated version of the real pl. 2 may be found on p. 84 of Stephen V. Grancsay, ed., *Master French Gunsmiths' Designs of the XVII–XIX Centuries, Reproduced in Facsimile* (New York: Winchester Press, 1970).

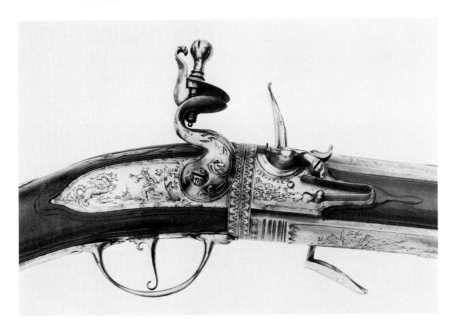

60 *Pair of Flintlock Pistols*

AUSTRIAN (FERLACH), ca. 1710

THE stocks of stump walnut are carved with relief borders and foliage and terminate in a dark horn tip. The cast, round gilt-bronze barrels have panels of chased floral decoration and a raised sighting rib. This is divided by the central relief panel; the rear portion is engraved *Thomas Hamerlitz*, the forward carries the integral blade front sight. The engraved barrel tang incorporates a hollowed rear sight. The locks have convex surfaces; the plate is of engraved and chased gilt bronze while the cock and battery are of chiseled iron; the cock bolt is of chased gilt bronze. The gilt bronze mounts are chased, engraved, and, excepting the buttcap and forward thimble, are pierced.

Thomas Hamerlitz is recorded as working in Ferlach (Carinthia) between 1698 and 1738, where numerous firearms were made and exported to Italy during the seventeenth and eighteenth centuries. Considering the proximity of Carinthia to the Venetian Republic, neither this export trade nor pronounced Italian stylistic influences in Ferlach-made firearms is at all surprising.

In these pistols the Italian flavor is shown in the novel concept of the barrel chasing, which imitates in bronze the chiseled iron plaques set in the stocks of Brescian firearms. These plaques are characterized by tightly compressed scrolling foliage enclosed within relatively symmetrical boundaries. This affinity to Brescian arms is further exemplified by the pierced and tightly scrolled design of the sideplate. Furthermore, the several masks incorporated within the chased design are certainly more Italianate than Germanic.

Provenance: Geoffrey Jenkinson, London, 1963.
Overall length, 19¼ in. (49 cm.); barrel, 13 in. (33 cm.); caliber, .58

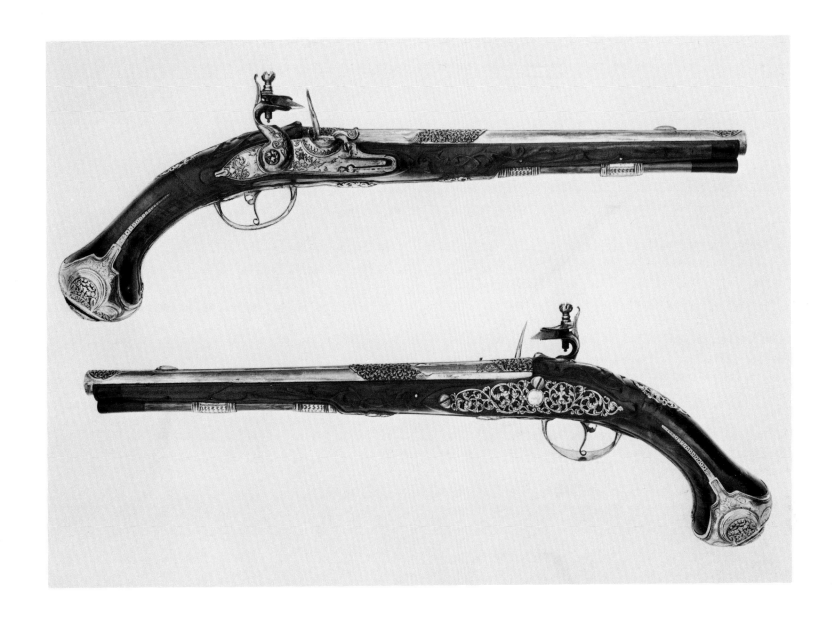

61 *Garniture of Flintlock Gun and Pair of Pistols*

GERMAN (BAYREUTH), dated 1733

THE stocks, of stump walnut, have relief carving and moldings and horn tips. Round damascus barrels, with side flats for approximately one-third of their length, have an almost full-length sighting rib terminating in a silver blade front sight. The locks have flat surfaces and are relief chiseled over a striated ground. The signature HOFMAN is engraved on the three lockplates enclosed in the V of the battery spring, and the inscription ·A· BAYREUTH· 1733· runs along the lower beveled edge of the plate under the battery spring. Cast silver mounts, chased in relief and engraved, have a gold mat background. The buttplate of the gun has the crowned monogram EADS of Ernst Augustus, Duke of Saxony. The original felt tompion with its wooden tip protects the bore of the gun.

At present there are sixteen known firearms by Hoffman, among which these are the earliest dated pieces.[1] This garniture is the product of several decorative traditions. The German damascus barrels, novel at this time (1733)[2] are restrained in design and rely for decorative effect on their figured pattern rather than on applied ornament. The silver mounts are in keeping with the new rococo style of German domestic silver of this period, while the stock carving, al-

though not as successfully designed, is likewise consistent. The maker of the mounts does not appear to have utilized published firearms designs. However, decorative elements such as symmetrical borders enclosing a mat ground and diaperwork are shown in de la Collombe's 1730 Parisian pattern book.

Although the form of the locks is quite modern, the chiseled hunting scenes continue, in both design and execution, a tradition of German ornamentation begun more than a century earlier. Likewise the washers for the lock retaining screws that substitute for the sideplate recall similar washers on the wheel-lock, while at the same time they give a false impression of a much later date. The quality of the chiseled hunting scene on the lock of the gun is superior to that of the pistol locks and indicates that the chiseling is the work of different artists. The pistols have full stocks, while the half-stock of the gun appears to be original.

Provenance: Ettersburg Castle; Theodor Jakobsson, Stockholm; Sotheby, May 10, 1932, lot 22; Fischer Gallery, Lucerne, November 29, 1972, lot 149.
Overall length of pistols, 17 in. (43.2 cm.); barrel, 11⅛ in. (28.2 cm.); caliber, .58
Overall length of gun, 53 in. (134.6 cm.); barrel, 38 in. (96.5 cm.); caliber, .63

---

[1] Hoff, *Feuerwaffen*, II, p. 145.
[2] Hayward, *Gunmaker*, II, pp. 95 and 117.

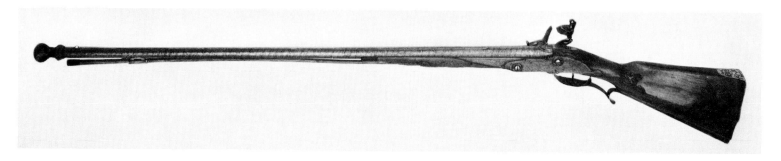

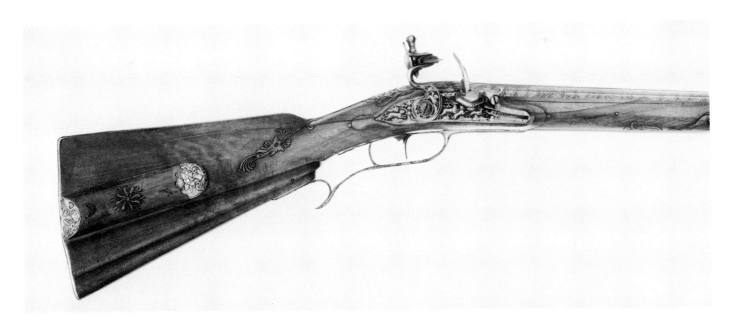

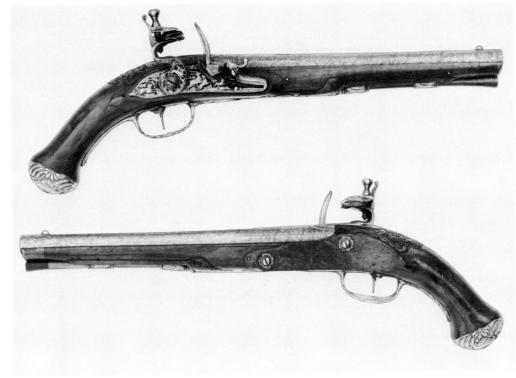

62 *Flintlock Rifle*

GERMAN, ca. 1735

THE full stock of stump walnut has relief carving and raised borders. There is a butt-trap with a sliding wooden cover. The full octagonal damascus or twist welded barrel tapers, then flares toward the muzzle. It is rifled with seven grooves and is fitted with an iron bar rear sight having a long leaf front extension and a simple brass blade front sight. The barrel-maker's mark, a gold-lined oval containing a six-pointed star surmounted by a man and the name G·H·ILLIN, is struck in the upper flat of the breech. The flintlock has flat surfaces, and a gilded external safety in the form of a grotesque mask is mounted behind the cock. It is engraved and chiseled in very low relief; the decoration of the plate represents Diana in her bath surprised by Actaeon. The double-set triggers have an adjustment screw, their plate is engraved with borders, is gilded, and terminates at the rear in a leaf finial. The mounts are of gilded brass. The pierced sideplate is cast in low relief, and the buttplate and triggerguard have leaf finials. There are three ramrod pipes, and the forestock terminates in a horn cap. The mother-of-pearl arms in the cheekpiece and the staghorn inlays on the cheekpiece and patch box cover are later replacements.

This barrelmaker's mark is not recorded, but Støckel lists an Illig or Illing as working in Bayreuth ca. 1740. It is certainly worth noting that the same engraving technique is used on the lock of this rifle and on the locks of the Hoffman garniture (No. 61), which were made in Bayreuth.

This type of short flintlock rifle is generally referred to as a Jäeger. This characteristic arm resulted from the introduction from France into Germany of the flintlock and the fowling piece buttstock. While these succeeded in displacing the indigenous wheel-lock and cheekstock, the raised cheek-piece was assimilated by the new arm. Various wheel-lock elements were retained—the rifle barrel form, the butt-trap, the double-set triggers—but the finger rest guard survived only slightly modified. The major development occurred in the 1680s, a period when the French flintlock forms were rounded and the buttstock had a slightly inflated appearance. This alien style had such a strong impact that Jäegers were made still utilizing the bulbous stock twenty to thirty years after its disappearance in France. The flat lock surfaces and faceted mounts of the "Bérain" style did not undergo the same delay and were introduced in the 1690s almost simultaneously with their appearance in France.

This lock draws one's attention because of the mythological subject of its engraving, although the human anatomy presented problems to the engraver that resulted in a naive depiction approaching folk art. On the other hand, the engraving of the cock is fairly representative of academic work of the time. The stock carving is of fine quality. The design of the relief-carved border around the butt-trap is strikingly similar to the patterns of brass patch boxes on early American rifles and seems to point toward the source of this design.

Provenance: Fischer Gallery, Lucerne, June 1961.
Overall length, 42⅛ in. (107.3 cm.); barrel, 27½ in. (69.8 cm.); caliber, .57

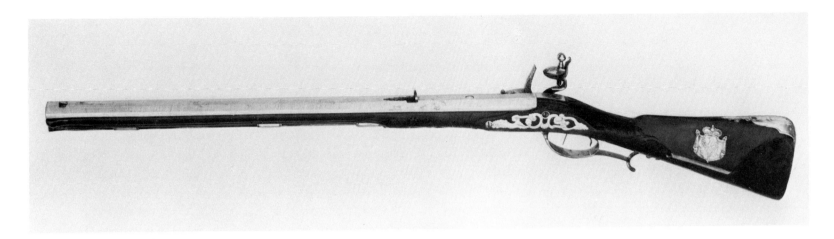

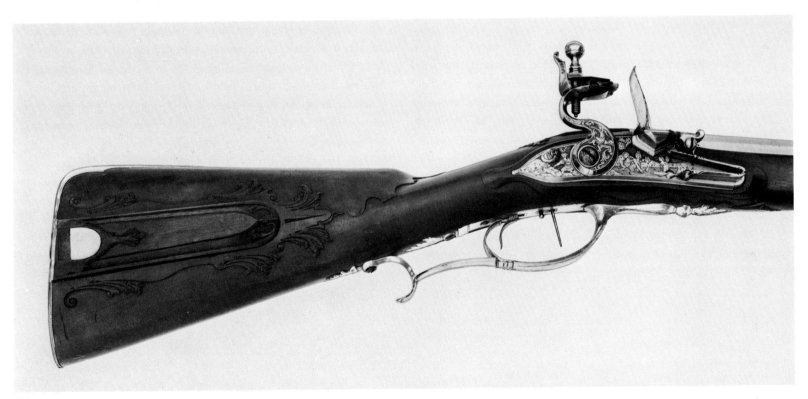

63 *Pair of Flintlock Pistols*

AUSTRIAN (VIENNA), ca. 1735

THE full stocks of stump walnut are carved with strapwork, foliage, and borders. The slightly flared round damascus barrels have two short relief panels on the upper portion separated by gold inlay. The touch holes are gold lined. The forward panel is inscribed in gold letters: FELIX MEIER IN WIENN. There is a gilt brass V rear sight at the juncture of the breech and tang and a brass blade front sight. The conventional flintlocks have flat surfaces that are engraved and chiseled with hunting scenes and foliate strapwork. The signature FELIX MEIER is engraved under the pan, and the continuation, IN WIENN, is on the plate to the rear of the cock. The latter is held by a gilt bronze-headed bolt. The gilt bronze mounts are engraved and chased with foliage and strapwork. Both the sideplate and the escutcheon are pierced. The wooden horn and brass-tipped ramrods are fitted with worms.

Felix Meier was one of several gunsmiths working for the Habsburg court at Vienna, where he died in 1739.[1] He is perhaps best known as being among the first to manufacture damascus barrels in imitation of Turkish prototypes.

These pistols display the typical Viennese approach to firearms ornamentation. Their locks are decorated with hunting scenes designed and executed in the same manner as on wheel-locks—the engraved figures are over a recessed and darkened mat background. This is to be expected since contemporary Austrian makers were manufacturing both wheel- and flintlocks contemporaneously. The typical strapwork design found overall seems to exhibit an *horror vacui* on the part of the Vienna smiths. In the case of the barrels of these pistols, this has been forgone in favor of the highly figured damascus twist. Overall, the quality of the locks and barrels exceeds that of the stocks and mounts. The sharply angled grip of these stocks suggests types popular later in the century, indicating that this pair may possibly be one of Meier's final works.

Provenance: Fischer Gallery, Lucerne, June 19, 1967, lot 118.
Overall length, 20½ in. (52 cm.); barrel, 14¼ in. (36.2 cm.); caliber, .65

---

[1] Schedelmann, *Die grossen Büchsenmacher*, p. 203.

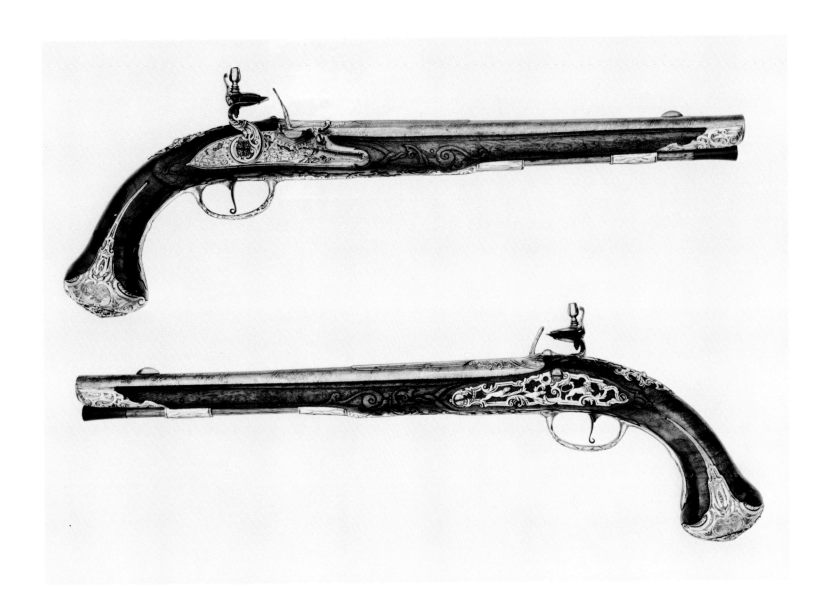

64 Flintlock Gun

GERMAN (ZWEIBRÜCKEN), dated 1744

THE full stock of stump walnut with relief-carved borders and foliage is inlaid with silver wire grotesques and scrolls. The round barrel has a very short octagonal section at the breech, forward of which is a hydra chiseled in bright steel and, above, Minerva against a gold damascened ground, followed by a fluted and gilded section. The remainder of the barrel is blued with damascened decoration at both ends of the sighting rib, which extends to the gilded iron front sight. The rib is signed in gold HEESZ A DEVX PONTS. The polished steel lock has flat surfaces that are relief chiseled with classical figures and animals against a gold ground. On the battery Jupiter is astride an eagle; on the cock, Leda; Neptune and Hercules are on the lockplate. The lockplate is signed on the lower beveled edge D. HEESS DEVX PONTS; a riband contains the date 1744. The iron mounts are decorated en suite; the separate buttplate extension has the chiseled figure of Diana.

While unrecorded, D. Hess must be one of the family of artisans who for several generations worked for the dukes of Pfalz-Zweibrücken. Despite its German manufacture, this piece is overwhelmingly French, even to the maker's frenchified "Deux Ponts." Nonetheless, under close scrutiny Hess's attempt to emulate Parisian style falls short, since such a display of mythological deities was passé following the abandonment of the Louis XIV classical style. While the quality of the chiseling compares favorably with Paris work, that of the wire inlay, which is restricted to the buttstock alone, a style developed in Paris in the earliest years of the eighteenth century, does not. Restricted wire inlay continued in vogue until the middle of the century and is illustrated in various Parisian pattern books of the period. Hess was working from at least one of these books—de la Collombe's 1730 edition from which the buttstock inlay is derived (see Lenk, *Flintlock*, pl. 129, no. 2). Most of the ornament, in fact, is closely related to, although not directly derived from, de la Collombe's book. The two-part construction of the buttplate also originates with the classical Louis XIV style, and is shown in pl. 5 of Simonin's 1685 pattern book. Hess has disguised the juncture with a border molding that passes just forward of the shell on the upper extension of the buttplate.

One puzzling feature of the stock is its spliced toe. While inset wood repairs to natural flaws are not uncommon in the making of a stump stock, such opposing grain as seen here is not usually encountered, and may indicate a later repair, although the inlay across the seam appears undisturbed. The escutcheon, chiseled with unidentified arms, has been altered or replaced during the gun's working life in order to accommodate the present arms.

Overall length, 58 in. (147.3 cm.); barrel, 42¾ in. (108.5 cm.); caliber, .63

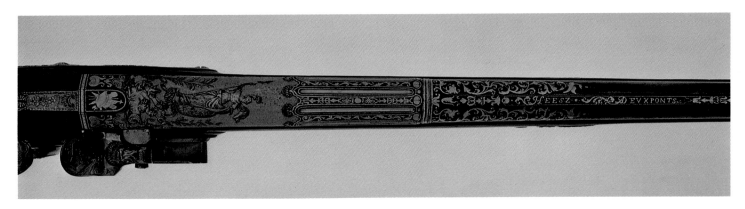

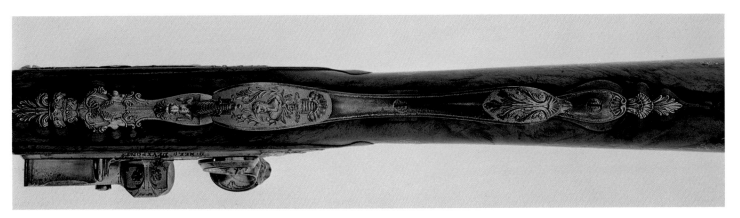

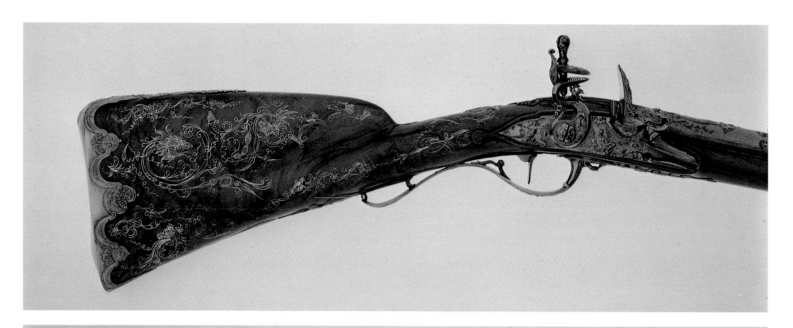

64

64

[165]

65 Pair of Flintlock Holster Pistols

BOHEMIAN (CARLSBAD), ca. 1750

THE stocks, of stump walnut, are heavily relief carved with rocailles and are inlaid with silver wire along the butt and forend. The round barrels have a sighting rib and side flats extending from a short octagonal breech. The barrels are blued and are decorated with floral damascening, principally around the breech, and have the gold block letter signature L. BECHER along the rib. The two gold breech stamps are not identified by Støckel as having been used by this maker. The bead front sights are silver, and the small rear sights are integral with the iron barrel tang. The locks have convex surfaces and relief-chiseled decoration and internal battery springs. The cast silver mounts are chased in high relief with military scenes and rococo designs.

During the second quarter of the eighteenth century, probably the most prestigious of the Carlsbad makers was Leopold Becher. A flintlock gun by Becher with both enclosed cock and battery spring in the Porte de Hal Museum, Brussels, and these pieces, which also have internal battery springs, show his inclination to experiment and to depart from regional stereotypes. On the other hand, the technique of casting an integral forward ramrod pipe and forend cap is quite common in the Carlsbad–Regensburg–Vienna triangle.

The design and decoration of the locks of these pistols are obviously inspired by chiseled firearms design in Western Europe in the 1650s. The lockplates, with military trophies and mounted warriors in relief occupying even the area normally covered by the battery spring, resemble their earlier counterparts. While the military theme is repeated in two versions on the chased sideplates, one of them has the feeling of designs in the first and second Simonin pattern books (1685, 1693). These two different military scenes are enclosed within identical rococo frames. This segregated combination of rococo and baroque design is departed from, however, in the escutcheon, which completely blends the two decorative styles. The other mounts are more contemporary with their uniform florid rococo elements. The stock carving shows its cultural affinity with Viennese rococo woodcarving in its preoccupation with the fanlike shell. However, the mask behind the tang recalls baroque design and relates closely to a like mask on the pair of pistols by Jan Knoop of Utrecht, ca. 1680 (No. 27).

Provenance: Sotheby ("the Property of Roy G. Cole"), June 15, 1970, lot 59.
Overall length, 16⅛ in. (41 cm.); barrel, 11 in. (28 cm.); caliber, .54

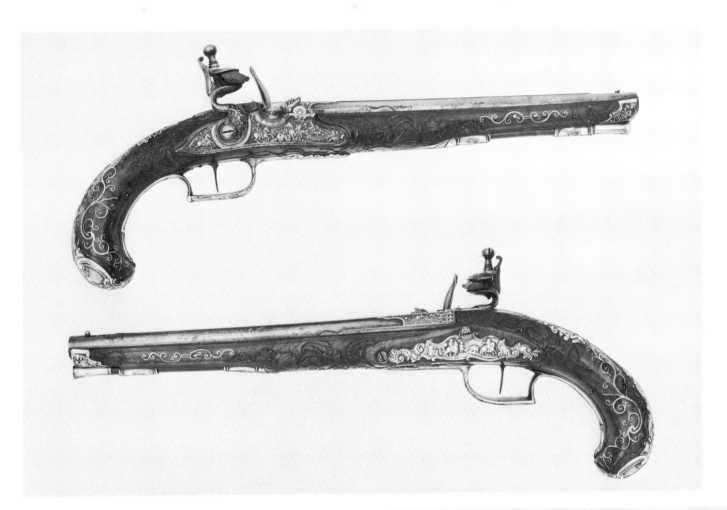

66 Double-Barreled Flintlock Gun

BOHEMIAN(?) (SKOTSCHAW), ca. 1830

THE walnut half-stock is carved in relief, inlaid with silver wire scrolls, and fitted with sling swivels. Tapered round damascus barrels are browned, joined with a concave rib, and inscribed in gold *Canon Damas*. Gold sunbursts are inlaid at the breech and surrounding the silver front sight. The post-1810 Liège, Belgium, proof mark is struck into the breech. The concave rear sight is integral with the tang of the breech block. The locks, with flat surfaces, have gold-lined rainproof pans and friction wheel battery springs. They are relief chiseled and engraved. Within an oval on the right lockplate is the gold signature *Wissneker*, while on the left is the inscription *in Skotschaw*. Silver mounts are chased and engraved, and the oval escutcheon is engraved with the monogram YLI. The original ramrod with its horn tip and iron worm is held by three pipes.

This maker is unrecorded; he may have been working in what is now Skuteč, Czechoslovakia. Wissneker was obviously a gunsmith of exceptional ability, and, while working within the cliché of Napoleonic style, he introduced a number of very individualistic elements on this gun. The most curious of these are the pierced scrolls forming the cock necks, which are duplicated by like projections behind the cock jaws and on the batteries.

Provenance: Arthur Yates, Costa Mesa, California.
Overall length, 47¾ in. (121.3 cm.); barrel, 32½ in. (82.5 cm.); caliber, .60

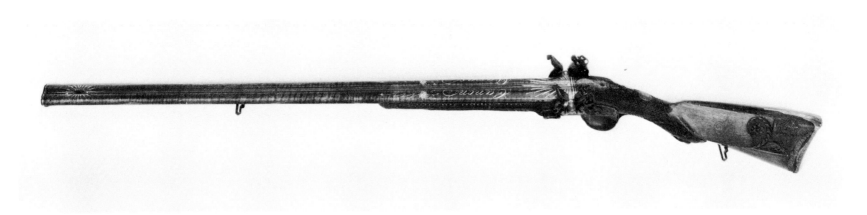

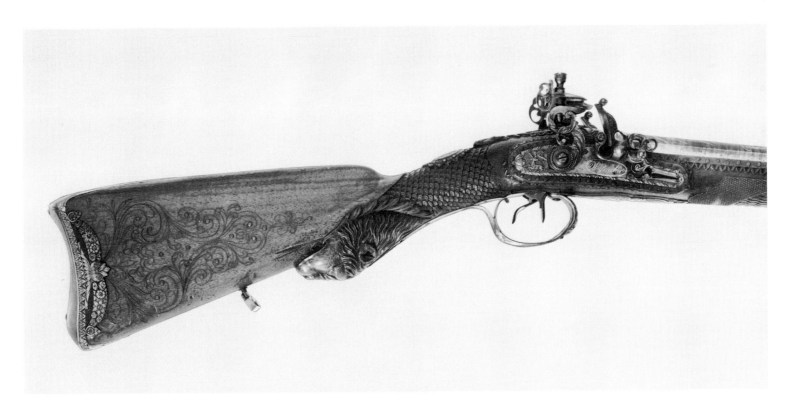

67 Cased Double-Barreled Shotgun

BOHEMIAN (PRAGUE), ca. 1850

THE stump walnut half-stock is heavily relief carved and has a cheekpiece. Double barrels of patterned damascus twist are inlaid with gold scrolls at the breech and are joined with a similarly decorated central sighting rib. The rib is inscribed in gold *A.V. Lebeda in Praze* between decorative inlay and has a silver bead front sight. Back-action locks are chiseled and inlaid with engraved gold; the right lòck is signed A.V. LEBEDA, the left À PRAGUE. The iron buttplate, triggerguard, and breech tang are decorated en suite with the locks. The triggerguard grip rail is of horn. Both stock and barrels have corresponding sling swivels. The rosewood case with German silver fittings has compartments containing a leather powder flask signed on the German silver spout *A.V. Lebeda, à Prague*; a shot flask with blued iron fittings; a wad cutter; a bullet mold; a screwdriver; a nipple wrench; and a ramrod. The covered compartment has a mainspring vise, brush, brass powder measure, engraved silver capper, and an ebony cap box with an engraved silver plate in the lid.

Anton Vinzenz Lebeda was born in 1795 in Czernowitz and died in Prague in 1857. He worked for Contriner in Vienna, and in 1820 was in the workshop of Mathias Brandis in Prague. He became a master in 1822 and subsequently produced a large group of rifles and shotguns for Emperor Franz Josef. He exhibited a variety of arms at the 1851 International Exhibition at London and at Brussels in 1856. Charles Claesen engraved and published arms designs from the Brussels exhibit. Pl. 28 of this collection shows a "Gothic" pistol made for the Shah of Persia by Lebeda Frères. The date 1857 on its hammer coincides with that of Anton's death.

This shotgun is of excellent quality; its most outstanding feature is the superlative stock carving that comprises both pseudo-Gothic and baroque revival elements.

Provenance: A. Goldberg, Los Angeles, California, 1963.
Overall length, 47½ in. (120.3 cm.); barrels, 32 in. (81.2 cm.); gauge, 12. Case length, 33½ in. (84.9 cm.); width, 9¾ in. (24.6 cm.)

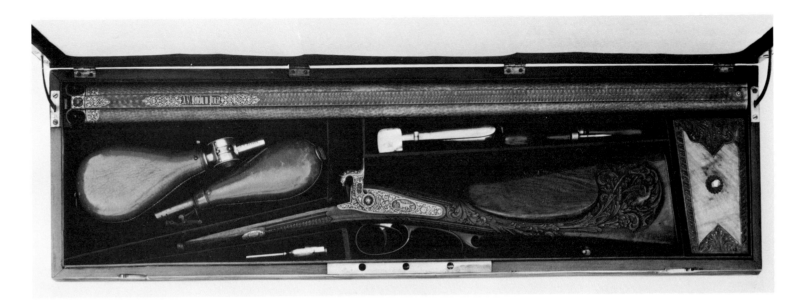

ITALIAN

ITALIAN firearms exhibit a strong native style that is characterized by decoration in chiseled and pierced iron in tightly composed floral designs incorporating grotesques and occasionally human figures. There are a few exceptions in which makers work in Western European styles, in some instances using French pattern books (see No. 73). In the majority of these, however, some influence of the native style remains detectable in the applied ornament or in the form of the piece.

The following arms represent the gunmaking areas of both Northern and Southern Italy. Northern production consisted of wheel-locks and snaphaunces of strong regional character, and flintlocks of both regional and international style. While not illustrated here, the snaphaunce, introduced in the seventeenth century, achieved such popularity that it became a nineteenth-century anachronism. In the South, long Spanish occupation possibly accounts for the popularity there of two versions of the miquelet lock.

68 *Pair of Wheel-lock Pistols*

ITALIAN (BRESCIA), ca. 1640

THE stump walnut stocks are inlaid with engraved iron tracery. Both stocks have a round paper label forward of the triggerguard with the legend *Royal Archaeological Institute*. The tapered octagonal barrels are fitted with an iron bar rear sight and a silver blade front sight. At the breech the upper left flat is struck with the gunmaker's mark, IG (Joseph Griffin, Støckel 3335), surrounded by the London view and proof marks. The lockplates have chiseled borders and are mounted with an external wheel. The dog neck and wheel retaining ring are fully chiseled, and the wheel arbor is surrounded by a chiseled rosette. The interior of both lockplates bears the stamped mark of Giovanni Antonio Gavacciolo (Støckel 427). The iron triggerguards are chiseled, pierced, and engraved, and the butts are encircled by a chiseled iron band. The pistols are fitted with simple iron belthooks, and the original ramrods have turned and chiseled finials.

This type of pistol, often with less decoration, is of a style popular in Italy during the first half of the seventeenth century. The generally diamond-shaped lockplate and the stock with pierced and engraved iron inlay, the quality of which may vary greatly, are characteristic of Brescian arms. Judging from the eighteenth-century English barrels, which by all indications were fitted new, these pistols seem to have enjoyed a remarkably long working life. Joseph Griffin probably made the barrels during the third quarter of the eighteenth century, and the stocks were altered in order to accommodate them. The most drastic alteration was the shortening of the forend, necessitating the construction of the abbreviated tracery forend caps. Considerable inletting was required for the long English tangs, which have encroached heavily on the upper stock inlay. The longer tang also forced the relocation of the tang screw. Two transverse screws that pass through each section of forend inlay secure the barrel to the stock. The forward screw utilizes the previous hole and loop mortise, while the rear was established when the barrel was fitted. The wood and metal surfaces of all of the alterations show evidence of considerable age. The most obvious reason why the barrels were replaced was because one of the originals burst. Early documents often note the bursting of cheap Italian barrels.

Provenance: Sotheby, April 19, 1963, lot 174.
Overall length, 15 in. (38 cm.); barrel, 9¼ in. (23.5 cm.); caliber, .51

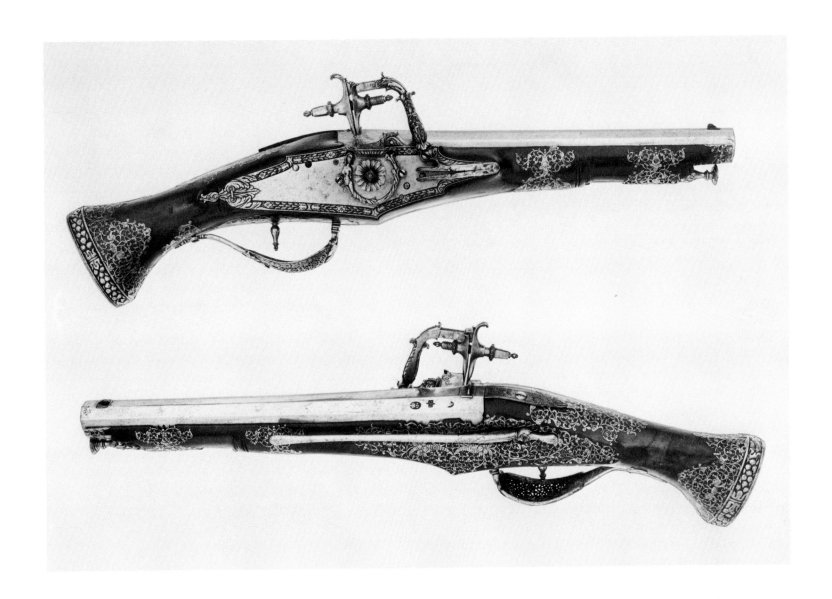

69 *Pair of Flintlock Pistols*

NORTH ITALIAN, ca. 1670

THE walnut stocks are carved with relief borders. The barrel is octagonal at the breech, followed by a very short sixteen-sided section and a round section set off by ring moldings; the remainder of the barrel is round. The top flat of the octagonal section is signed LAZARINO COMINAZZO, while the two flanking flats are decorated with longitudinal moldings. Convex lockplate surfaces are engraved, and the cock and battery have relief-chiseled volutes. The flat iron sideplates are pierced, engraved, and fitted with an iron belt-hook. The triggerguard finials are pierced and engraved, while the remainder of the iron mounts are simply engraved. The finials of the original ramrods are turned and engraved.

Lazarino Cominazzo, whose signature is on the barrels, came from the illustrious barrelmaking family, originally of Gardone, whose name became associated with Brescia for almost two centuries. Various members of the family used this same signature with slight variations through successive generations. The fame of Lazarino barrels was such that the Spaniard Alonso Martínez de Espinar, writing in 1644, states, "In Italy long ago worked a master, called Lazari Cominaz; he made very good barrels; because of the fame they enjoyed many others have made and do make very bad barrels, and put on them the name of Lazari Cominaz, as did the legitimate one; and of these badly made ones many have burst and caused great misfortune."[1] John Hayward has indicated that there is a group of fakes easily recognized be-

cause they do not conform to the Cominazzo style.[2] Considering the international popularity of Cominazzo barrels and the supply of fine barrelsmiths, there are undoubtedly excellent foreign counterfeits still masquerading as legitimate. These barrels, which appear to be legitimate, may be the work of the Lazarino Cominazzo, who was executed for political reasons in 1696.

These good quality pistols are particularly graceful because of their long barrels and slender lines. They reflect vividly the influence of French design on the firearms of Northern Italy. With their pierced and voluted cocks, the locks are associated with the published designs of Thuraine and le Hollandois (1660) as is the general form of the trigger-guards, which are attached by wood screws in the Italian manner. Consistent with the French approach, the maker has omitted the heavy three-dimensional chiseling so associated with Brescian firearms. His adherence to French style is not total, since turned or heavily sculptured ramrod finials are very Italian as is the heavily pierced trigger backplate—in this case a dolphin whose tail extends to the tip.

Provenance: John F. Hayward, London, 1963.
Overall length, 22 in. (56 cm.); barrel, 16 in. (40.1 cm.); caliber, .52

---

[1] Alonso Martínez de Espinar, *Arte de ballestería y montería* (Madrid, 1644).

[2] Hayward, *Gunmaker*, I, p. 193.

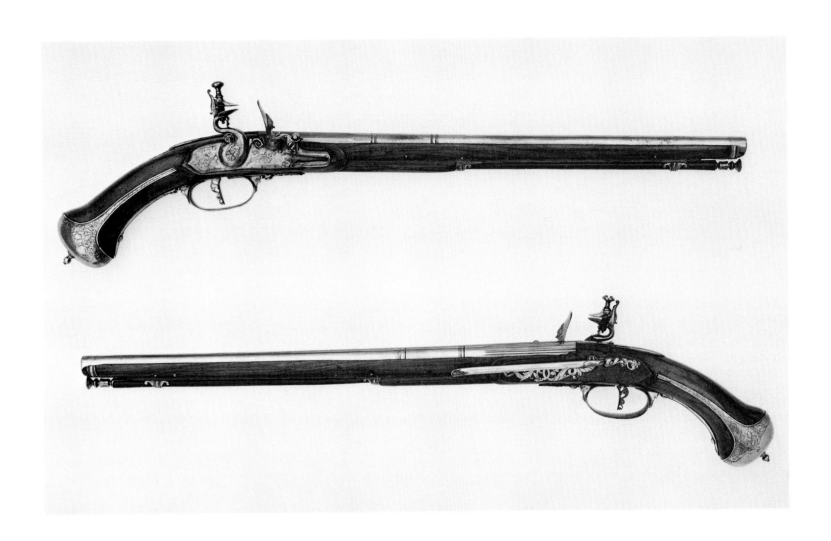

70 Pair of Flintlock Pistols

ITALIAN (BRESCIA), ca. 1680

THE stocks are of walnut with relief-carved borders and are inlaid with pierced and chiseled iron plaques. The octagonal breech section of the barrels is decorated with longitudinal moldings, and both are signed on the top flat LAZARINO. Just forward of this are ring moldings separated by floral engraving, and the barrels continue round to the muzzle. There are shallow rear sights that are integral with the tang and silver blade foresights. The locks have convex surfaces that are relief chiseled and engraved with foliate designs incorporating serpents, and the plate is engraved between the cock and battery spring with the signature *Gio. Batta. Zanetti*. The iron mounts are pierced and chiseled in relief in the same manner as the stock inlay. The original ramrods terminate in chiseled iron monkey figures that match the triggers.

Nolfo di Carpegna has suggested that the barrel signature LAZARINO may refer to Lazzaro Cominazzo, who was born in 1646. Other locks are recorded by Giovanni Battista Zanetti, but nothing further is known about him.

The decoration of these pistols places them in a group that is generally considered to be Brescian. Characteristic of this group are the coarsely chiseled and pierced iron plaques in which the scrolling foliage is contained within symmetrical perimeters.

Also associated with this group are the intertwining biting serpents with lumpy bodies, and the beaded borders sometimes defining the limits of decoration on buttcap, triggerguard, and other parts. The fully sculptured monkeys, which frequently appear on triggers and ramrod finials, stand apart from the other decoration and are directly related to identical figures on Italian stiletti. Another group of highly decorated Italian firearms of the same period incorporates similar simianlike figures more prominently into the overall decoration. These, however, are not of the French flintlock type as are those in the group under discussion.

These pistols, as well as the remainder of the group, adhere to the basic style of Thuraine and le Hollandois, but their applied ornament is entirely Italian. Similar mounts, possibly from the same hand, may be seen on a pair of double-barreled pistols in the Odescalchi Collection (62–63).

Provenance: Sam Bloomfield, Palm Springs, California, 1970. Overall length, 15½ in. (39.3 cm.); barrel, 9½ in. (24.1 cm.); caliber, .48

71 *Flintlock Pistol*

ITALIAN (MILAN?), ca. 1700

THE stock is entirely of iron, chiseled in relief and engraved with flowers. On the top of the grip is a flying winged figure holding a garland with the script signature *Longa*. The barrel is round and has relief chiseling at the breech and a raised sighting bead. The convex lock is relief chiseled with masks and foliage as are the preceding parts, and beneath the pan is engraved the name VILLALONGA. The sideplate is pierced and chiseled, and the rear lock screw also holds the steel belthook. The triggerguard, buttcap, and applied tang and trigger surrounds are similarly decorated.

The iron stock is unusual, and the engraved depiction of pommel spurs is an especially interesting touch. Flanking the "spurs" is floral engraving that seems to have been inspired by Marcou's designs (1657). The pierced and relief-chiseled tang surround might appear to be a novel feature, but its design source is the 1660 pattern book of Thuraine and le Hollandois. Almost every plate of this book illustrates an elongated decoration designed to surround the barrel tang. Some of the patterns are to be executed in carved wood, others in sheet-metal inlay. Here Villalonga has achieved in iron the three-dimensional effect of wood carving, thereby com-

bining these two concepts. He has taken part of the design of the surround shown in pl. 8 of the aforementioned pattern book for the surround on this pistol. Chiseled ornament on the buttcap and battery indicates that he was also strongly influenced by these elements from the same plate. The classical head medallion, with its garland frame decorating the triggerguard bow, and a similar head on the boss of the pommel further reflect designs from Thuraine and le Hollandois.

The lock of this pistol is very closely related to a slightly earlier detached lock in the Odescalchi Collection (940) signed by Giovanni Azzurro of Milan. Moreover, the floral engraving of the Azzurro lock is remarkably like that of the Villalonga pistol. The form of the triggerguard and some of the barrel chiseling seem to be the latest elements of the design and place this pistol near the close of the seventeenth century.

Provenance: M. Lemmons, Brussels, 1969.
Overall length, 13 in. (33 cm.); barrel, 7¾ in. (19.6 cm.); caliber, .53

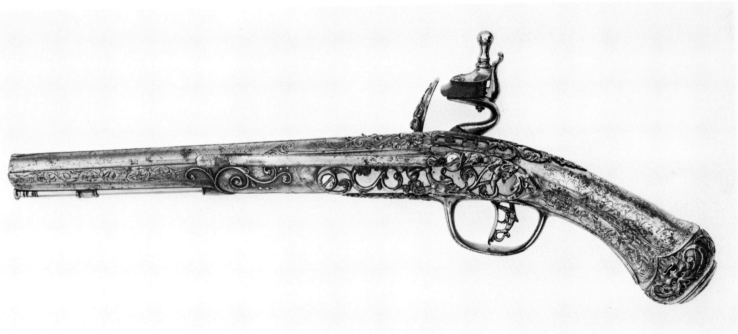

72 *Pair of Flintlock Pistols*

ITALIAN (TUSCAN), ca. 1715

THE burl maple stocks have relief borders and scrolling foliage. The barrels are octagonal and round with an acanthus leaf girdle at the transition where a raised sighting rib begins and extends almost to the muzzle. Stamped in the breech are the gold marks of Pistoia; the touch holes are gold lined. The convex surfaces of the lockplates have engraved hunting scenes and borders and the signature *Lòrenzoni* engraved above the finial on the battery spring. The cocks (one replaced) and batteries have relief chiseling; the batteries are constructed so that the pancovers can remain closed while the steels are raised as a safety feature. The safety is operated by pressing the forehead of the relief-chiseled mask on the face of the battery. All mounts are gilt brass, and the sideplate is pierced and chased in relief while the pommel, escutcheon, and triggerguard are only chased and engraved. The pommel terminates in a grotesque mask; the ramrod pipes have bulbous turnings. The original ramrods have worm tips (one missing).

Michele Lorenzoni is perhaps best known for the numerous flintlock repeating arms that he produced. These so-called Lorenzoni system firearms are possibly the invention of Giacomo Berselli of Bologna, as Dr. Arne Hoff has suggested. In any event, Lorenzoni was the leading Florentine gunsmith, and as such provided many arms to the Medici court. Lorenzoni adhered to the Louis XIV classical style to the apparent exclusion of Italian national styles, which incorporate a heavy reliance upon folk themes and are often crowded and coarsely executed. These would have found little favor in the noble circles for which he worked.

These pistols provide a good example of French fashion; hunting scenes on the locks suggest that Lorenzoni may have been using the Simonins' 1693 pattern book. These pistols conform generally to the style of the pattern book, and the hunting scenes appear to be actual simplifications of the lock ornament engraved on pl. 12. The sunken panels on the pommels, however, have a close resemblance to the new style first introduced in Paris in the 1690s (see No. 12), but which did not gain popular acceptance until the early years of the eighteenth century.

Provenance: Geoffrey Jenkinson, London, 1970.
Overall length, 16¼ in. (41.2 cm.); barrel, 10¼ in. (26 cm.); caliber, .56

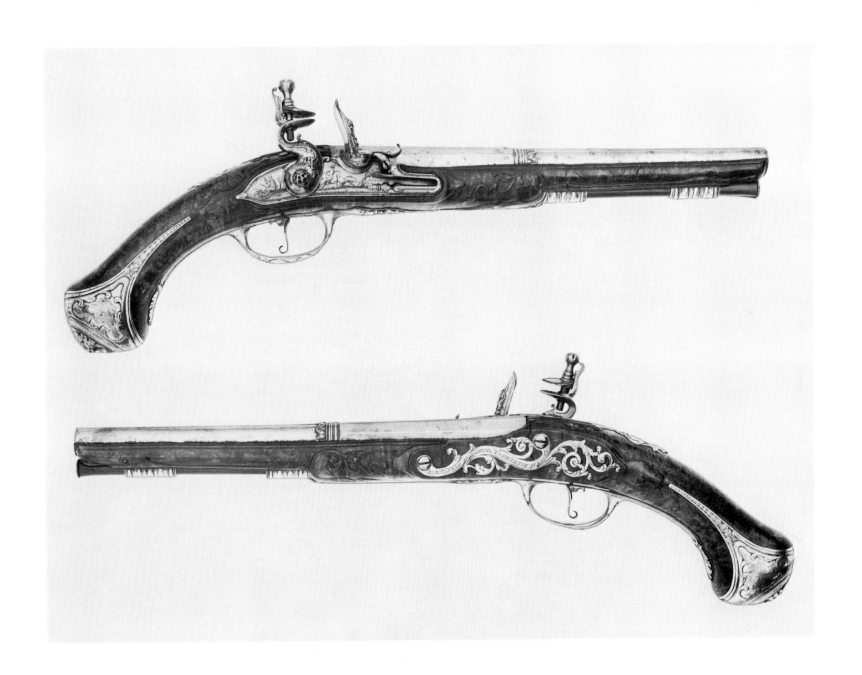

73 *Flintlock Breech-Loading Repeating Gun*

ITALIAN (PIEDMONT), ca. 1720

THE half-stock is made in two parts: the buttstock of stump walnut has borders in relief, and the brass forestock has embossed and engraved scrolls within raised borders. The barrel is octagonal for two-fifths of its length, then it gradually turns to round. A raised sighting rib begins forward of the breech and continues just beyond the silver bead front sight. Ring moldings surround the breech, and forward of these is an engraved bust. The brass breech mechanism is chased in scroll designs enclosing the engraved inscription TOMASO LEFFER VALENZA DEL PO. The lock has a brass plate and pan; its flat surfaces are engraved with trophies of arms and foliage, while the brass cock retaining bolt and the steel battery are chiseled. The chased and engraved mountings are of brass. A trigger forward of the triggerguard releases the magazine loading mechanism. The magazine consists of two brass tubes under the barrel forward of the lock, which are loaded with powder and ball respectively. To operate, the muzzle is raised, the forward trigger is depressed, and the barrel and magazine section is rotated to load powder and ball into the chamber and prime the pan.

The earliest known magazine gun of this type, dated 1668, is attributed to Leffer presumably because of the Valenza del Po inscription on its lockplate. Michele Lorenzoni and others also produced both pistols and longarms utilizing this system, and by the beginning of the eighteenth century it was even being made in America. Close study of the decoration of this piece reveals that Leffer was using Simonin's 1685 pattern book in its 1705 reissue that incorporated plates by de la Collombe. This edition consists of the original title plate with an altered inscription including the new date of 1705. Plates 2 through 8 are restrikes from the original book, while 9 through 11 and 13 were engraved by de la Collombe and illustrate the new style. Plates 9 and 11 are dated 1702 and 1705 respectively. While not displaying gun designs, pl. 12, a battle scene by Simonin, is original to the 1705 edition. Leffer has copied exactly designs for the sideplate and escutcheon (pl. 6) and for the panels covering the magazine (pl. 8) from the earlier portion of the book. From the revised edition come the top extension of the buttplate and the chased decoration enclosing his signature on the brass breech section (pl. 11). Leffer was using this book a number of years after its publication as is shown by the design of the lock and the form of the butt.

Overall length, 61½ in. (156 cm.); barrel, 44 in. (111.7 cm.); caliber, .58

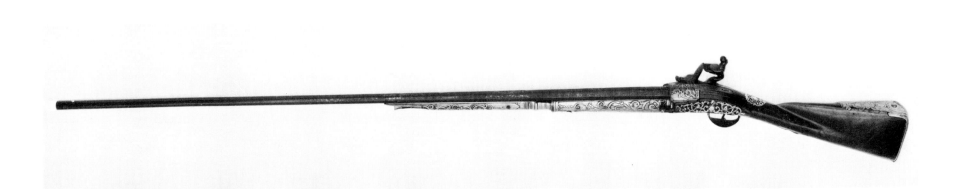

74 Miquelet Lock Pistol

ITALIAN (NAPLES), ca. 1755

THE walnut stock is inlaid with pierced and engraved silver sheet in foliate designs incorporating two grotesque masks. The barrel is in two equal stages divided by a ring molding; the breech section is beaded, the forward is round with a medial sighting bead running the length of the section. The Spanish-style miquelet lock is engraved with borders and foliate designs. The pan and cock bridles are gadrooned. The iron triggerguard, which serves as the forward tang screw, is inlaid with an engraved silver band. The forend terminates in an engraved silver cap; the plain iron sideplate is fitted with a belthook. The ramrod is of iron with simple turnings.

This pistol is an Italian copy of a popular Spanish Catalan prototype. They were produced almost exclusively in the town of Ripoll near Barcelona, and today are usually referred to as "Ripoll" pistols. They were produced there by the thousands during the entire eighteenth century, but the period of their greatest production appears to center around mid-century.

Far fewer Italian copies were made. They may be distinguished from their Spanish counterparts by a generally shorter barrel and an elongated pommel as opposed to the more heart-shaped profile of the Ripoll pommel. Also different is the construction of the spurred triggerguard. In the Italian examples, the rear extension joins the grip rail at nearly a right angle, while on the Spanish guard the angle is decidedly acute. The Italian guard may also differ from the Spanish by having an engraved plate of silver or brass inlaid longitudinally in the bow. Italian examples frequently have engraved silver stock inlay, as seen here, rather than brass as occurs on all known Ripoll pistols of this type. Unlike the Ripoll examples, the Italian stocks are sometimes carved and the engraving of the inlay is bolder and of better design.

There were two types of Spanish Ripoll ball-butt pistols. During the seventeenth century their stocks were completely metal sheathed and engraved or inlaid overall with pierced and engraved metal. Early in the eighteenth century, the engraved metal inlay became restricted to the elongated forend cap, the tang surround, the pierced pommel inlay, and the triggerguard surround. This Italian group was copied from the second type of Ripoll pistol. Its introduction into Italy apparently followed the return in 1735 of the Kingdom of the Two Sicilies to Spain and the coronation of a Spanish prince as king of Naples.

Overall length, 11 in. (28 cm.); barrel, 7$\frac{1}{16}$ in. (18 cm.); caliber, .59

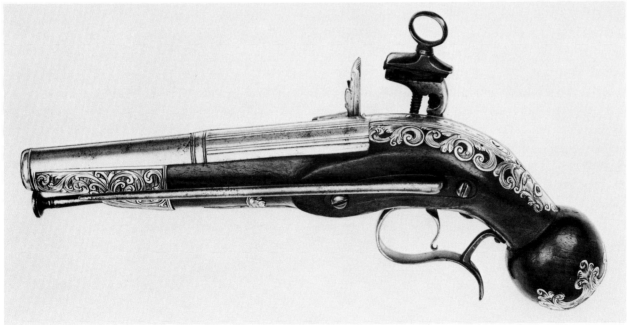

75 *Miquelet Fowling Piece*

THE full stock of crotch walnut has relief borders and is inlaid with silver wire and engraved silver plaques. It terminates in a horn tip with a molded iron band. The blued barrel is octagonal at the breech, and round following the turned and chiseled transition. The double initials EM:ES are engraved on the bottom flat at the breech. Engraved gold inlay is concentrated around the breech and at the transition, and the top flat bears the inlaid gold inscription ANNO 1770. A gold front sight is also surrounded by a slight gold inlaid design. The touch hole is bushed with gold. Two gold stamps are struck into the upper breech: the CR monogram of the king of Naples (Carolus Rex) appears above that of the Royal Manufactory, FAB.R. DI NAP. (Støckel 814). The lock of the Spanish *a la moda* type is chiseled, inlaid with gold, and engraved; the pan is gold lined. Both cock and battery are retained by bolts with chiseled and damascened heads, and the plate is struck with the gold stamp F.R. DI NAP. (Støckel 816). All iron mounts are chiseled over a gold damascened ground, while the sideplate and two barrel bands are additionally pierced. The escutcheon has the inlaid engraved gold monogram FR formed by intertwining ribbons. The engraved inscription MICHELE BATTISTA FECIT within an engraved floral cartouche is on the back of the buttplate.

All known works of Michele Battista span a period of only eighteen years, from 1760 to 1778. Except for a single pair of pistols made in Avellino in 1760, Battista seems to have worked exclusively for the Royal Manufactory, where most of his arms were produced for royalty. This factory was founded just outside Naples at Torre Annunziata in 1757 by Carlo, king of the Two Sicilies. He was the younger brother of King Fernando VI of Spain and succeeded his brother there in 1759 as King Carlos III. His son, Ferdinando I, then ruled in Naples until 1825. This gun appears to have been made for Ferdinando, whose monogram is engraved in the crowned escutcheon. There is, moreover, a remarkable similarity between much of the decoration of this piece and another made by Battista for Ferdinando in 1775. While not the most opulent, this arm shows the highest quality of workmanship of any of the known Battista guns. The pseudo-French style is to be expected because Battista was working in Naples for an essentially Spanish court that had been strongly francophilic since the Bourbon accession in 1700. The French style is especially evident in the Spanish *a la moda* lock and the triggerguard. The style of the silver sheet and wire stock inlay is very like French designs of the 1660s and bears little relation to known French-inspired Spanish arms. One outstanding exception to the French orientation is the very English form of the buttstock.

The original monogram stamp of the Royal Manufactory incorporated the initials CR (Carolus Rex). Carlo abdicated in 1759 and was succeeded by Ferdinando, thereby necessitating changing the stamps to FR. Rather than make new FR stamps, at first the CR was altered by the addition of a superimposed F. This altered stamp was used on a pair of Battista pistols of ca. 1770 in the Metropolitan Museum, New York (No. 26.259.5,6). A new FR stamp was in use by 1772 when Battista dated a pair of fowlers now in the Real Armería, Madrid (K168–169). Although dated 1770, the barrel of this gun bears the original CR stamp, and it must therefore be concluded that the barrel remained in storage in blank form for at least eleven years before being decorated and mounted on this fowling piece.

Provenance: Eric Vaule; Herbert Ratner, Greensburg, Pennsylvania.
Overall length, 51 in. (129.5 cm.); barrel, 36¼ in. (92 cm.); caliber, .60

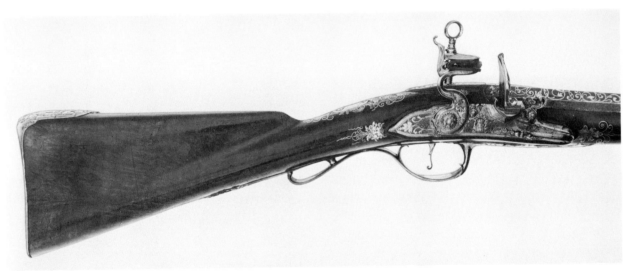

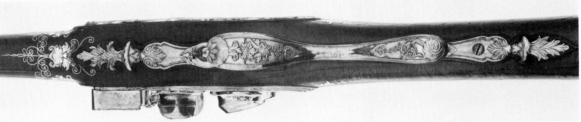

[189]

76 Flintlock Gun

ITALIAN (TURIN), ca. 1815

THE stump walnut stock has a raised cheekpiece and is relief carved and checkered. The carved decoration consists of neo-classical moldings, a sculptural stag's head with glass eyes terminating the grip, and an eagle with the silver arms of Savoy to the rear of the barrel tang. The round barrel has two side flats that extend one-third of its length and a sighting flat that terminates about three inches from the muzzle. The shallow open rear sight is integral with the hooked breech tang, and the foresight is a silver blade. Stamped in the breech are three gold marks: the crowned cross of Savoy flanked by rampant bulls. Forward of these, inlaid in gold, are an oval plaque engraved with the figure of Diana, the crowned intertwined monogram VE, and the inscription *Lecler a Turin*. The flat surface lock has a rainproof pan and a roller on the battery spring. It is engraved, and the signature Lecler a Turin appears on an oval gold plaque within an engraved wreath on the plate below the pan. The mounts are silver; the triggerguard and buttplate have the oval mark LV of the Assay Master Luigi Vernoni, the Turin Standard Assay Mark D9 flanking a crowned eagle (Denari 9, or 9/12 silver alloy),[1] and the rectangular maker's mark LC, undoubtedly that of Lecler. The triggerguard is engraved and chased with a lion on its forward post. An inlaid gold oval on the bow has the engraved crowned arms of Savoy. The buttplate and two-piece sideplate are engraved, and there are two sling swivels and a rosewood ramrod tipped with mother-of-pearl.

Støckel refers to a Lecler (Leclerc, Le Clerc) as royal gunsmith in Turin, and also to a Giovanni Battista Lecrer, royal gunsmith, who may be the same gunmaker. It is not known whether this Lecler was related to the Paris gunmaking family of Le Clerc, but he signed this arm in French and his barrels are marked in a manner similar to theirs.

This gun was made for Victor Emmanuel I, king of Sardinia, who ruled between 1802 and 1821. His monogram appears on the barrel. From 1814 he resided in Turin in Savoy, leaving his brother Carlo Felice as viceroy in Sardinia. This piece bears the silver marks of Luigi Vernoni and D9, both of which were not introduced until 1814. While it was made in Italy for an Italian ruler, this gun is designed entirely in the Napoleonic Empire style.

Provenance: Fischer Gallery, Lucerne, June 17, 1964, lot 275.
Overall length, 50⅜ in. (128 cm.); barrel, 35 in. (89 cm.); caliber, .61

---

[1] Personal communication from Mr. Claude Blair, Victoria and Albert Museum.

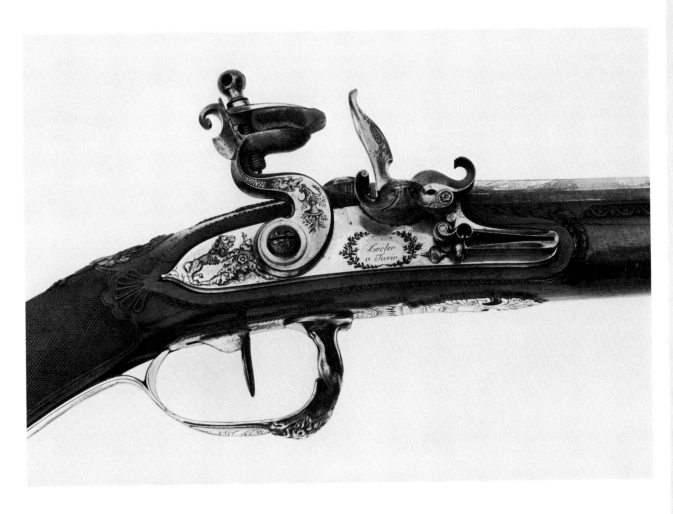

77 *Miquelet Gun*

ITALIAN (NAPLES), dated 1828

THE full stump walnut stock is carved on the forend and grip with a running chevron design that ends on the underside of the grip in a grotesque animal head. The barrel is damascus twist. Its octagonal breech has light gold inlay and recessed panels that terminate just to the rear of a transitional ring molding, from which point the barrel continues sixteen-sided to the muzzle. The upper flat of the breech is struck with the mark of the Royal Manufactory of Naples (Støckel 814), the royal cipher (Støckel 819, but with the F crossed), and three fleurs-de-lis (Støckel 821). On the left flat of the breech are the crowned stamped initials BS; the engraved signature *Domenico Battista* is on the underside of the tang. The blued flat surfaced lock is chiseled, engraved, and inlaid with gold. The pan and recessed pancover are gold lined, the internal lock parts are chiseled, and the inner surface of the plate is engraved *Domenico Battista* along the lower edge and is struck with the same crowned initials BS as on the barrel. A gold stamp of the royal cipher, FR, is on the exterior between the cock and pan. The blued iron mounts are also gilded, chiseled, and engraved, and the buttplate is inscribed within an engraved oval *R.ᴸ Fab.ᵃ d'Armi in Torre Annunz.ᵗᵃ* 1828. The original ivory-tipped ramrod is retained by three pipes inlaid with gold and engraved.

Domenico Battista possibly represents a second- or third-generation descendent of the renowned Michele Battista, who began working in this same factory some sixty years earlier (See No. 75). The small BS mark may be that of Battista or of some other workman at the Manufactory. A very similar slightly defaced mark is associated by Støckel (2103) with Naples ca. 1817. The late date of this gun shows that the Neapolitan royal cipher logically remained unchanged as a manufactory mark after the death of Ferdinando I in 1825, since he was succeeded by his son Francesco I. A number of arms were also made here which have the manufactory mark but lack the royal cipher. One possible explanation may be that some of these pieces date from the two periods of French occupation: 1799–1802 and 1805–1815.

The Napoleonic influence is evident in this piece in its pistol grip buttstock with grotesque carving, patterned "checkering," triggerguard with sculptured front post, and two-piece sideplate.

The pierced throat of the cock of this lock is typical of nineteenth-century Neapolitan miquelet locks. Its origin may be found in the crescent neck of the Spanish Catalan lock, which goes back to the late seventeenth century. It appears unchanged in Naples in the eighteenth century, taking on a C-scroll form, the ends of which eventually touch to form an enclosed area. Once the design of the lock is fully developed, cheaper versions appear that omit the piercings.

Provenance: Arthur Yates, Costa Mesa, California, 1966.
Overall length, 50⅞ in. (129.2 cm.); barrel, 36½ in. (92.7 cm.); caliber, .72

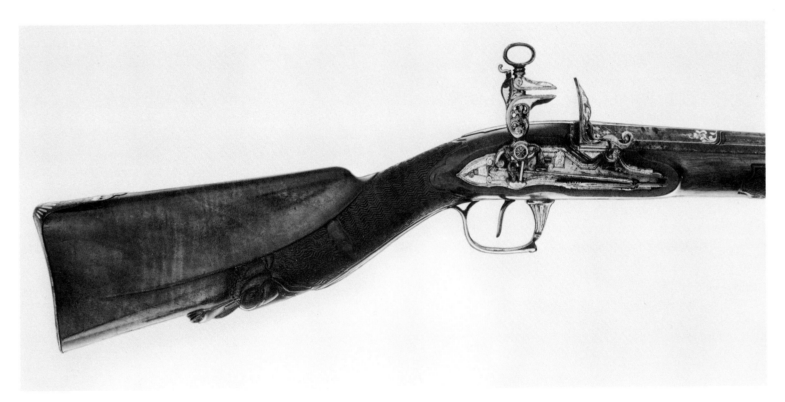

77

HISPANIC

FROM the advent of the snaplock in the earlier part of the seventeenth century the miquelet lock "*a la española*" dominated Hispanic firearms (see No. 79). This situation did not change until the accession of a French king—Felipe V—in Spain in 1700 forced a consciousness of French style, at least in the metropolitan areas. Even then, the French flintlock was accepted only in its external appearance, and conservative Spanish makers clung doggedly to the miquelet sear. A combination of the two systems resulted in what was known at the time as the "*a la moda*" locks (see No. 78). While hundreds of *a la moda* locks exist today, the extreme scarcity of Spanish flintlocks of French type testifies to a strong conservatism. Not until near the end of the eighteenth century did the typical Spanish miquelet undergo any significant change; this was to alter its contoured lockplate to one of French flintlock form to produce the "*tres modas*" lock (see No. 81). In general, Hispanic arms show a greater decorative emphasis on the metal parts as opposed to the selection of the stock wood and its ornament. There are occasional exceptions, some of which may be seen in this collection. Following the demise of the Empire style, Spanish gunmaking entered a state of decline until, in the 1830s, the royal gunsmith Eusebio Zuloaga made a conscious attempt to revive sixteenth-century designs and techniques.

78 *Pair of Flintlock* (a la moda) *Holster Pistols*

SPANISH (MADRID), ca. 1710

THE stocks, of burl maple, are carved with foliage, relief borders, and moldings. The barrels are in three stages: the breech is octagonal with a gold gunmaker's stamp with one name effaced, four gold thistles, and the engraved signature ṄCOLAS; the short adjacent area is sixteen-sided with the visible flats alternately engraved and gold inlaid; transition to the round forward half is provided by turnings and chiseling. Several relief turnings reinforce the muzzle. Along the forward portion a sighting rib is engraved BIS MD (Madrid). The touch hole is gold lined. The flat surfaces of the locks are relief chiseled and engraved. The plates are stamped between the cock and the pan with Bis's gold mark (Støckel 60), and along the lower edge is engraved the block letter signature NICOLAS BIS MD. The pierced iron sideplates are chiseled in relief, and the cartouche bears a chiseled classical bust. Relief chiseling and engraving decorate the triggerguards and pommels. The barrels are secured to the forestock by a chiseled and pierced iron band that also holds the gold front sight. This band is retained by a spring latch that is engraved en suite with the pommel spurs. The original ramrods have a turned ivory tip.

These pistols are of a type called "saddle pistols" (*pistolas de arzón*) in eighteenth-century Spanish inventories. The locks are of the type contemporarily named *a la moda* (*francesa*) which, except for their peculiarly Spanish sear arrangement, emulate the French flintlock. This mechanism is popularly known today as the "Madrid lock," although in the eighteenth century it was manufactured throughout Spain. The flat lock surfaces reflect the New "Bérain" style.

Both locks and iron furniture were decorated in a combination of styles suggesting Parisian designs from the pattern book of Claude and Jacques Simonin (1693), while the decoration of the triggerguard is a slight elaboration of a design by de la Collombe (1705). It is interesting to compare this triggerguard, most certainly derived from de la Collombe's pattern book, with the triggerguard on the Piraube pistols of 1697 (No. 12), whose maker undoubtedly provided de la Collombe's original design. The almost identical survival of Piraube's concept, this remote in time and place, through the vehicle of the pattern book is remarkable. The high relief classical masks on the pommels are Napoleonic in style and character of execution, and were probably added during that era. The maple stocks represent a departure from the cherry and walnut traditionally used in Spain, and again are a concession to the current French taste.

Nicolás Bamproyssem y Bis (Bis von Preussen?) was "a German by Nationality"[1] who studied in Madrid under the royal gunsmith, Juan Belén. He succeeded to the post of gunsmith to Carlos II upon his master's death in 1691. On the accession in 1700 of Felipe V, Spain's first Bourbon monarch and grandson of Louis XIV, Bis was resworn and served until his own death in 1726. He was replaced by his son-in-law and pupil, Matías Baeza.[2] During the War of the Spanish Succession he produced, besides these pistols, the magnificent

---

[1] Isidro Soler, *Compendio historico de los arcabuceros de Madrid* (Madrid, 1795), p. 46.

[2] James D. Lavin, *A History of Spanish Firearms* (London: Herbert Jenkins, 1965), pp. 96–98.

pair made for Felipe V that are now in the Tower of London (XXI-1629, 1630). Subsequently Bis became in 1713 the first royal gunsmith ordered "to devote himself solely to works for His Majesty." To Bis is attributed the invention of what was to become the common Spanish practice of manufacturing barrels from horseshoe ends, "which makes him worthy of perpetual memory."[3]

The sudden craze in post-1700 Bourbon Spain for everything *a la francesa* certainly accounts for the heavy French flavor of existing Bis pieces. He employed in his shop the 1705 edition of the Parisian pattern book engraved by Claude

Simonin and de la Collombe with little or no apparent time lag.[4]

At the beginning of the Peninsular War (1808), fifty-three guns by Bis were in Madrid's Real Armería, while several pairs of pistols by him were kept in the royal stables. Today only one complete fowler remains in this collection.

Provenance: Sotheby, February 19, 1973, lot 275.
Overall length, 18 in. (45.7 cm.); barrel, 12½ in. (31.7 cm.); caliber, .64

[3] Soler, *Compendio historico*, p. 46.

[4] James Duncan Lavin, "The French pattern book of Nicolás Bis, Gunsmith to Felipe V of Spain," *Connoisseur*, CLXV (August 1967), pp. 274–279.

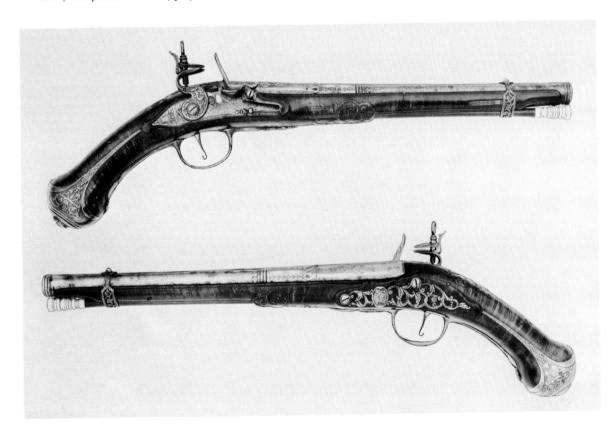

79 Pair of Miquelet Pistols

SPANISH (RIPOLL), ca. 1780

THE walnut stocks are lightly carved with rococo designs around the tang. Engraved sheet silver inlays are in the shape of large crowned preening birds on either side of the miniature gunbutt grips; a trigger plate pierced in floral designs extends to form the triggerguard finial; and a small floral plate is at the ramrod's point of entry. The silver buttcaps overlap and encircle the butt, and, together with the sheet silver engraved sideplates, are permanently attached to the stock and may be considered a part of the inlay. The barrels are eight-sided at the breech with slightly rounded facets separated by ribs and inlaid with gold floral scrolls. The mark of the barrelmaker LLORENS POVS is struck in the upper breech above his countermark, the arms of Barcelona. The barrel becomes round at the midpoint forward of a single turned ring and bead molding, and a sighting bead extends from this to a similar molding that reinforces the muzzle. A silver barrel band fastens the barrel to the forend. The miquelet locks *a la española* (with external mainspring, cock and battery bridles, and wasp-waisted lockplate) are engraved with rococo designs and have some background stippling. The eternal mainsprings have relief-chiseled volutes at their point of attachment. Both lockplates are inscribed IPH ÐOP RIPOLL along the lower edge. The silver triggerguards are engraved with a rose on the bow. The iron belthooks are held by the lock retaining screws; the original ramrods have turned ivory tips.

These late eighteenth-century pistols represent the persistence of tradition in the Catalan area, where only elements of international style encroach upon earlier popular forms. The *a la española* lock predominated. Engraved rocailles give a unity to the parts, which in fact have been produced by at least three different hands in two different cities, a common enough practice in Catalonia.

The lockmaker Joseph Deop, undoubtedly a member of the large Deop gunmaking family of Ripoll, is unrecorded in Ripoll archives. He seems to have been the principal supplier, however, of gunlocks of all forms to various Barcelona smiths from as early as the second quarter of the century. The barrelmaker Llorens Pous is recorded by Graells as an arms contractor in Barcelona in 1770.

Provenance: W. Keith Neal, Warminster, England, 1963.
Overall length, 12½ in. (30.2 cm.); barrel, 7¼ in. (18.3 cm.); caliber, .69

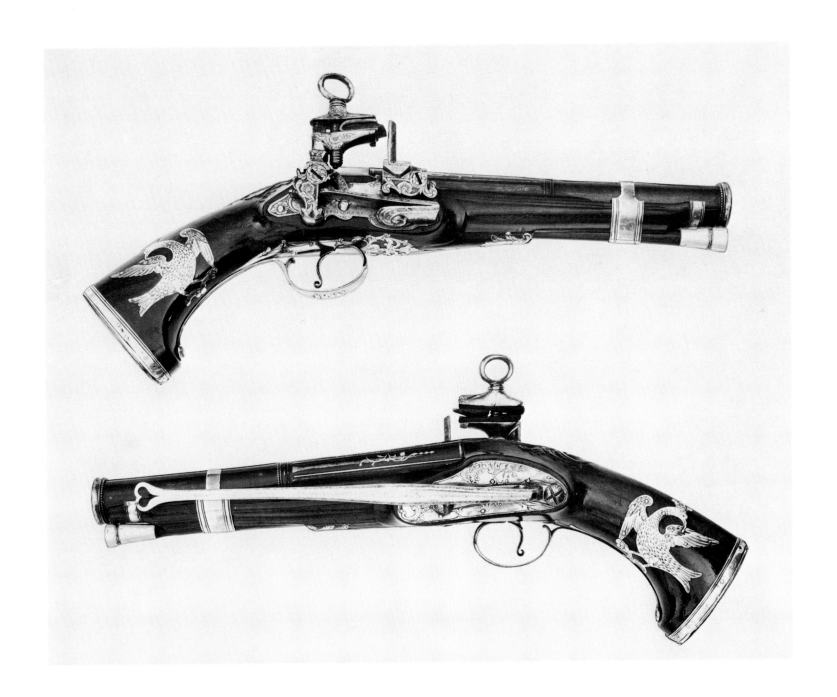

80 Miquelet-lock Blunderbuss Pistol

SPANISH (RIPOLL), dated 1784

THE darkened walnut full stock is inlaid overall with engraved and pierced silver plaques of animals, foliage, and human figures; adjacent areas are decorated at random with silver nails. The belled iron barrel is octagonal overall, although at approximately midpoint the flats shift so that the forward portion is exactly opposed to the breech end and forms a hog's back along the top. The barrel is inlaid with foliate designs in engraved brass, copper, and silver, enhanced by the addition of some more modern engraving. The brass-lined maker's mark, PACHECO crowned, is stamped into the upper breech and is surrounded by stamped, brass-lined arrows and fleurs-de-lis. The barrel tang is entirely covered with engraved sheet brass. There is an engraved inscription on the lower breech flat: *Se acavaron A 16 marzo de 1784* ("They were finished on March 16, 1784"). The miquelet lock is of the *a la española* type, but here it is made for left-hand mounting. The iron trigger is sculptured in the shape of a serpent with brass eyes, while the silver triggerguard and buttplate are modern replacements. The original ramrod, with a worm and silver baluster tip, has a retaining catch at its forward end. The iron belthook has a pierced finial.

The barrel inscription implies that this pistol was one of a pair, a supposition that may be strengthened by the unusual feature of its left-hand lock. The design elements of the stock inlay are loosely derived from formal seventeenth-century patterns, which enjoyed a belated popularity only in this region of northeastern Spain. Thus, the Habsburg double eagle is incorporated into the forend inlay more than three-quarters of a century after the demise of the last Spanish Habsburg ruler. The only concession to modern taste are the small diaper-engraved plaques along both sides of the butt.

These odd blunderbusses and similar carbinelike pistols were apparently quite popular in Spain during the eighteenth century and are depicted in a number of drawings by Goya. They were manufactured principally in Ripoll (province of Gerona) near the French border as well as, to a lesser extent, in several surrounding towns. The name Ripoll has since come to indicate various types of arms peculiar to this Catalan area in form and decoration.

Provenance: Sotheby, July 21, 1969, lot 185.
Overall length, 16½ in. (42 cm.)

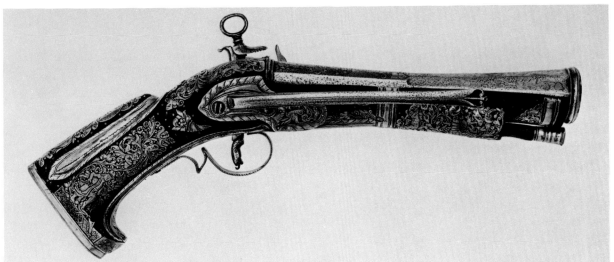

81 Miquelet-lock Pistol

SPANISH (EIBAR), ca. 1810

THE walnut stock is finely checkered in panels along the grip and has relief moldings of beads and scallops. The blued barrel is octagonal at the breech where it is stamped with the crowned maker's mark, BVSTINDVI. The upper flats are inlaid overall with gold floral scrolls and birds, to which outlines and details have been added by engraving. The round forward half is decorated with alternating gold spirals of stars and husks. Two moldings, a chiseled band at the midpoint and cannon turnings at the muzzle, are enhanced by twisted wire inlay. The *tres modas* miquelet lock retains much original bluing and engraved gold inlay; it is also signed BVSTINDVI in gold. Its pan and pancover are both gold lined. Mounts are of blued chiseled steel with a gilded background. The triggerguard is signed in gold ALBERDI across the back of the bow. There are two ramrod pipes. The iron pommel strap extends upward along the grip to the tang of the false breech.

Several generations of the Bustindui family worked in Eibar (in the province of Guipúzcoa) and are recorded from the middle of the eighteenth century. This pistol is undoubtedly the work of Juan Esteban Bustindui, the son and probable disciple of Agustín Bustindui, who, already practicing in Eibar, went to Madrid to study for a time under the royal gunsmith, Joaquín Celaya (d. 1760). Juan Esteban's house and shop were described by G. de Jovellanos after his visit to Eibar in 1791. Jovellanos states, "His fame rests on the excellence of his barrels, although he manufactures all parts. He works for various grandees and lords of the court, for America, for England, France, Russia and other places, from where there frequently come commissions."

More than one signature on an Eibar gun is not unusual because of the extreme specialization existing in the trade in this area of Spain. However, in this instance it is noteworthy that another luxury arm bears the same combination of signatures. A shotgun in the Real Armería, Madrid (K.166), is also signed by Bustindui on the barrel, and by Alberdi on the lock and buttplate. The gun was part of a gift commissioned by the province of Guipúzcoa for Fernando VII in 1814.[1]

The general appearance of this pistol reflects the Napoleonic era in which it was produced. Particularly obvious are the spiral decoration of the forward barrel section and the carved stock moldings which, on the grip, enclose checkering. The shield shape of the cock bridle, the keys retaining the barrel, and the roller on the cock heel are features usually associated in Spain with the post-Peninsular War (1808–1814) period. Engraving of barrel inlay of precious metals was practiced in Eibar and other provincial areas, but the engraving of inlaid metal was not typical of Madrid. A quite unusual feature of this barrel is its completely encircling chiseled and damascened transition, the lower half of which is concealed by the stock.

Provenance: W. Keith Neal, Warminster, England, 1963.
Overall length, 13¾ in. (35 cm.); barrel, 8⅜ in. (21.3 cm.); caliber, .66

---

[1] Gregorio de Mugica, *Eibar* (Zaraus: Editorial Icharopena, 1956), pp. 96–97.

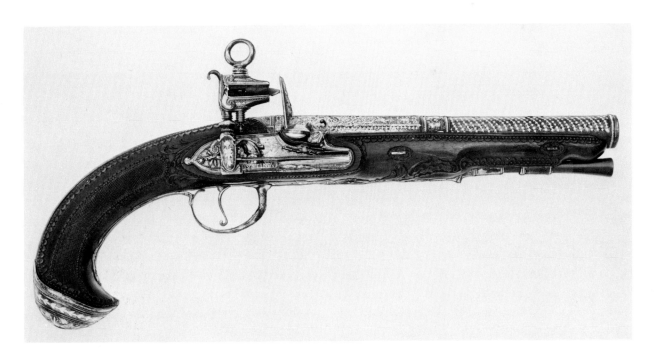

82 Miquelet-lock Gun

SPANISH (EIBAR), ca. 1810

THE crotch walnut full stock has relief-carved borders and floral carving about the lock, tang, and ramrod entry. The barrel is octagonal for about two-fifths of its length and continues round to the muzzle. Transition is made with turned moldings and chiseled acanthus leaves. Inlaid floral designs of engraved gold decorate the barrel, and the gold mark (Støckel 1182) and countermark (a rampant lion facing left) of the maker, Zarandona, are struck into the top flat of the breech surrounded by three gold fleurs-de-lis. The initials L. A. are inlaid in gold and there is a gold-lined touch hole. A raised open rear sight is integral with the tang section of the hooked breech; the front sight is a silver bead. The *tres modas* miquelet lock has friction wheels on the heel of the cock and on the battery foot, and the pan is gold lined. The lock parts are chiseled in relief, and the gold gunsmith's mark is repeated on the lockplate between the cock and battery. The original striated battery has been refaced with smooth steel. The mounts are of silver and, excepting the two barrel bands, are decorated with chased and engraved designs on a gilded ground. The triggerguard also bears the maker's mark. A screw on the underside of the buttstock and a forend swivel are designed to hold a sling.

In contrast to the normal practice in Eibar of attaching the barrel to the stock with pins, Zarandona has used barrel bands in the Madrid manner. He has also given the deluxe treatment to the barrel by continuing the chiseling and damascening of the transitional girdle entirely around its circumference. The carving around the tang continues the rococo tradition, while the bead and scalloped borders are Napoleonic in style. The unbalanced design of the sideplate appears to combine the more typical Eibar plate (see Bustindui pistol No. 81), with the sideplate featuring the medallion midway between the two lock mounting screws. The exaggerated voluted terminal on the grip rail of the triggerguard is unusual. This guard construction, with its double attachment at the rear, originated in Paris in the mid-eighteenth century and, slightly modified, became common on Spanish firearms. At the time this gun was made, the guard had ceased to be fashionable on French arms. A diminutive take-down fowler was presented by Zarandona to Queen María Luisa of Spain before 1808 (Real Armería, Madrid, K.167).

Provenance: Frank E. Bivens, Los Angeles, California, 1964.
Overall length, 52 in. (132 cm.); barrel, 36½ in. (92.7 cm.); caliber, .67

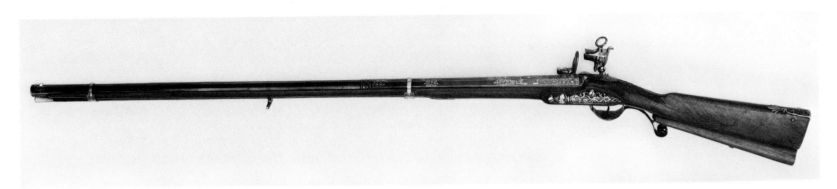

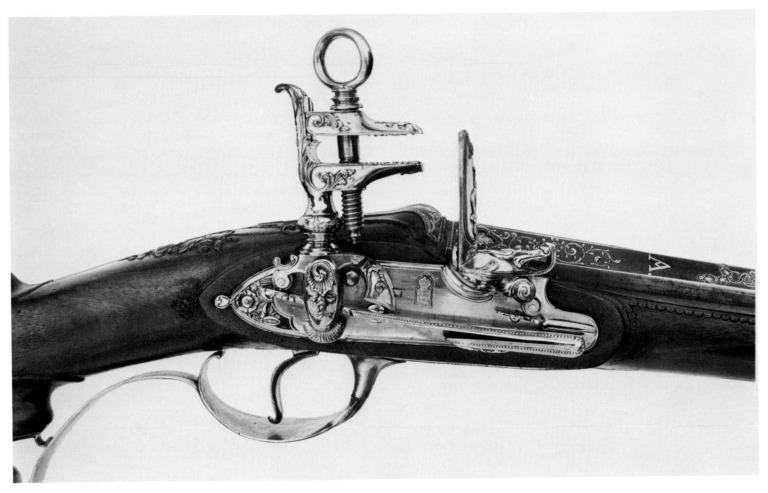

83 Miquelet-lock Gun

PORTUGUESE (LISBON), dated 1820

THE half-stock of stump walnut is carved with foliage and borders in relief and is inlaid with silver wire. A presentational verse begins on the left side of the buttstock and continues on the right:

> Por prenda esta Arma se deo
> Que o prazer, e a ira ascende;
> Porque nestes dois extremos,
> Dá morte, e della defende.

> (As a gift this Arm has been given
> That for pleasure or ire it serve;
> For in these two extremes,
> It gives death, and from it defends.)

The browned barrel is octagonal for two-fifths of its length, turning to round following a turned and chiseled girdle. Engraved gold inlay covers most of the octagonal section, and there is light inlay at the transition and surrounding the iron sight, which has a gold bead. The muzzle is slightly flared. The barrel is retained by a hooked breech and a single key, and the exposed forward section has an iron rib to support the ramrod. The gold mark and countermark of Verissimo de Meira (Støckel 229, 230) are struck in the breech, and the top flat is inlaid with the inscription FEITA EM LISBOA, NO ANNO DE 1820. The miquelet lock of Castilian style, called in Portugal *de invenção*, has flat surfaces and engraved gold inlay. The lockplate and mainspring are finished bright; the remaining parts are blued. A gold maker's mark, MALAQUIAS Jᴱ [JOZÉ] DA COSTA, is struck on the plate between the cock and pan, and his name is engraved again on an inlaid gold plate on the battery. A large friction

wheel on the upper mainspring leaf connects with the heel of the cock. The blued iron mounts have engraved gold inlay, and the unidentified arms of the owner are inlaid on the bow of the triggerguard. The ivory ramrod tip is inlaid with ebony dots and has a light wood collar.

Verissimo de Meira, whose name appears on the barrel, became master of the Royal Manufactory of Lisbon in 1757 and held this post until his death in 1792. Since this barrel bears what appear to be his legitimate marks but is dated 1820, it must be assumed that it was decorated en suite with these mounts. It is entirely possible that this barrel was stored unused in the Manufactory these many years. Little is known about da Costa, who obviously was a very competent maker. He probably worked in the Manufactory also, where it is likely that this arm was made.

The general form of this gun conforms closely to that of mid-eighteenth-century Portuguese arms, while the decorative details are quite modern. Typical of the former is the straight tang with its surrounding areas well above the level of the small. This results in a boxiness of the lock mortise accentuating the thinness of the wrist that contrasts with the broad "Spanish" buttstock. Unlike the tang surround, which contains strong rococo elements, the borders around the lock and mounts are crisply carved in Napoleonic style. The geometric wire stock inlay and the gold inlay of the mounts are very modern and seem to anticipate designs that were to develop fully toward the middle of the century.

Overall length, 53½ in. (135.8 cm.); barrel, 38½ in. (97.8 cm.); caliber, .63

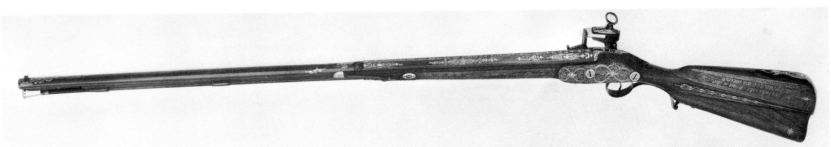

84 *Pair of Percussion Pistols in Mahogany Case*

SPANISH (EIBAR?), ca. 1855

THE walnut stocks have borders in relief enclosing panels of incised parallel lines in the manner of checkering. The blued octagonal barrels turn to round at about the midpoint. They are decorated with damascening, engraved gold inlay, and have a stylized sighting rib that widens at the beginning of the round section to enclose a chiseled fawn's head and terminates in a reinforced muzzle. On the upper flat of the breech appears the gold-inlaid inscription *Eusebio Zuloaga Arcabº de S.S.M.M.* ("Eusebio Zuloaga Gunsmith to Their Majesties"). The patent breeches have integral percussion bolsters chiseled with volutes in high relief. The blued locks are chiseled in relief, and are inlaid and damascened with gold. The hammer is sculptured in the form of a dog's head. The blued iron mounts are also damascened and inlaid with gold. The sideplates have chiseled iron ornaments en suite with the lockplate; the forward post of the triggerguard is chiseled in the shape of a small animal, possibly a fox. Ebony ramrods have blued and inlaid iron tips and a cleaning slot in the opposite end. The blue velvet lined mahogany case is fitted with a flask, bullet mold, screwdriver, and nipple wrench, all blued and gold inlaid en suite with the pistols.

Eusebio Zuloaga was born in Madrid in 1808, the son of Blas Zuloaga of Eibar, gunsmith to the royal family. Between 1822 and 1833 Eusebio worked and studied, first under his uncle Ramón Zuloaga in Placencia, then with his father in Madrid, Lepage in Paris, and at the factories of St. Etienne. In 1834 he became assistant to his father in the Royal Armory in Madrid where, on Blas's death in 1852, he succeeded to the post of royal gunsmith to Isabel II. About 1840 he founded a factory at Eibar, and it is known that he also practiced privately in Madrid. He died in 1898.

The plural "Majesties" in the inscription shows that these pistols were made after Isabel II's marriage in 1846. The design and decoration of these arms are strikingly similar to those on pls. 39 and 40 of Charles Claesen's compilation of designs of arms exhibited at the Brussels exposition of 1856. These plates, representing designs by an "M.P. Zuloagat," are probably those of Eusebio's son, Plácido, a designer, metalworker, and damascener who apparently exhibited there. Eusebio exhibited not only firearms but also all types of chiseled iron and damascened domestic accessories (centerpieces, inkstands, and so forth) at most of the major expositions during the 1850s and 1860s. The sculptured animal heads on the hammers and triggerguards are also similar to designs in Claesen's book. These two details have been formed with the skillful use of the chisel without the aid of polishing, which gives them a harsh, possibly rustic feeling in contrast to the formality of the remainder of the design.

The bullet mold is unusual because its sprue cutter is formed at the front rather than in the usual position between the handles. The powder flask is a stylized version in iron of the sixteenth-century German flask formed from staghorn.

Overall length, 16 in. (40.06 cm.); barrel, 9¾ in. (24.8 cm.); caliber, .66

84

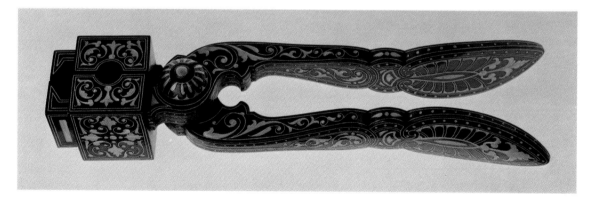

IN the seventeenth century Silesia consisted of eighteen principalities within the Austrian Empire occupying areas of Bohemia, Germany, and Poland, with the majority of these lying within Poland. The city of Teschen, in the principality of the same name, maintained a large manufactory of fire-arms well recorded in early inventories. It was situated in the southeast corner of Silesia on the border between modern Poland and Czechoslovakia and ethnically was more Polish than Bohemian. In 1920 the town was divided between the two countries, becoming the Polish Cieszyn and the Czecho-slovakian Tesin.

Firearms manufactured here during the seventeenth century are characterized by a deviate form of the German cheek-stock often called hind's foot (No. 85). This is normally combined with a peculiar lightweight wheel-lock having external mainspring, wheel, and chain. In many cases both dog and mainspring bridles are of brass sheet, which covers a large area between the arms of the springs and provides a sur-face for rather crude engraving. The rifled barrel is of un-usually small caliber and it appears that these distinctive arms were used for hunting small game. The name Tschinke was used in Poland as early as 1672 to designate this type of arm. A late seventeenth-century flintlock example in the Correr Museum, Venice, shows that the genre paralleled the long life of the German wheel-locks.

The two other types shown are radical departures from the Tschinke form, nevertheless, the stock inlay is so closely related in design and execution that they may represent par-allel manufacture in the same town. This inlay is composed primarily of staghorn interspersed with disk-shaped stylized strawberries of mother-of-pearl. In staghorn there are en-graved plaques, animals, and grotesques against a crowded ground of scrolling tendrils and dots. In some instances the Polish eagle is inlaid opposite the lock or on the cheekpiece. The source of ornament is suggested by a signed and dated inlaid wooden coffer in the Wallace Collection (A 1345). Its inscription shows that it was executed by the gunstocker Jean Conrad Tornier in 1630 in the Alsatian town of Masevaux, only forty kilometers northwest of Basel, Switzerland. The sophistication of the inlay on this chest as compared with that of the Silesian arms probably indicates that Tornier was much closer to the source of design than the Silesian gunstockers.

85 *Wheel-lock Rifle*

SILESIAN (TESCHEN), ca. 1650

THE full cherry stock is inlaid overall with engraved staghorn and mother-of-pearl. The plain octagonal barrel is slightly flared and is fitted with a bar rear sight and a bead foresight. It is rifled with six grooves. The lock, with its external mainspring, wheel, and chain, is lightly engraved. A push button between the dog and pan releases the pancover, and a similar button at the rear of the lock manually engages the sear. This button passes through a large flat bridle that covers the bend of the mainspring, and a similar bridle covers the dog spring. The iron triggerguard has three finger grips and a spade-shaped finial at the front.

This rifle, called Tschinke, represents a type of small caliber, light hunting arm generally considered to have been manufactured in Teschen, a Polish town on the Bohemian border. Contemporary references identify Teschen as the source of these rifles, and the town apparently maintained a large export trade. Considering the number of surviving examples, and the variations in their ornament and construction, it is probable that they were also made throughout a larger area of Eastern Europe.

The most characteristic features of the Tschinke result from its intended use. The lock has the majority of its works externally mounted since the slender stock and barrel will not accommodate the internal mechanism of a conventional wheel-lock. The unusual profile of the buttstock, sometimes called hind's foot, finds a close parallel outside this area in the buttstock of Scandinavian arms (see No. 88) and probably indicates the northward extension of the sphere of influence of the Tschinke. Certainly many Scandinavian arms exhibit Central European characteristics.

The inlay of this rifle is typical of the majority of pieces in the group. While profuse and attractive overall, the quality of its design and execution is not exceptional. The wheel-locks are usually of mediocre quality and often are coarsely decorated with overlaid brass tracery.

Provenance: W. Keith Neal, Warminster, England, 1963.
Overall length, 44½ in. (113 cm.); barrel, 34 in. (86.3 cm.); caliber, .33

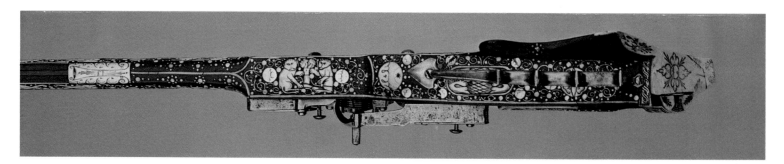

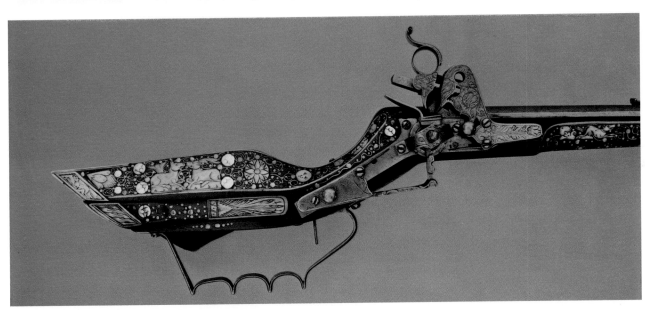

86 *Pair of Wheel-lock Rifles*

SILESIAN (TESCHEN), *ca. 1650*

THE fruitwood full stocks are inlaid with engraved staghorn and mother-of-pearl and have a butt-trap with a sliding wood cover inlaid en suite. The unmarked octagonal barrels are rifled with eight grooves and are engraved at the breech with rude swirls. They are equipped with an iron bar rear sight and a brass blade front sight. The plain convex locks have an external wheel and a button pancover release. The long iron triggerguards are plain and have three finger grips. The iron ground balls are fitted to the stock heels, which are covered with engraved staghorn buttplates.

The stock inlay of these rifles is closely allied with that of the Tschinke (No. 85). However, these gently curved stocks are more gracefully designed than the usual Tschinke hind's foot stock with its somewhat erratic profile. Moreover, the quality of their inlay is greatly superior. The barrels are tapered and flared in the German fashion.

Provenance: Frank E. Bivens, Los Angeles, California, 1975.
Overall length, 32½ in. (83 cm.); barrel, 23 in. (59 cm.); caliber, 34

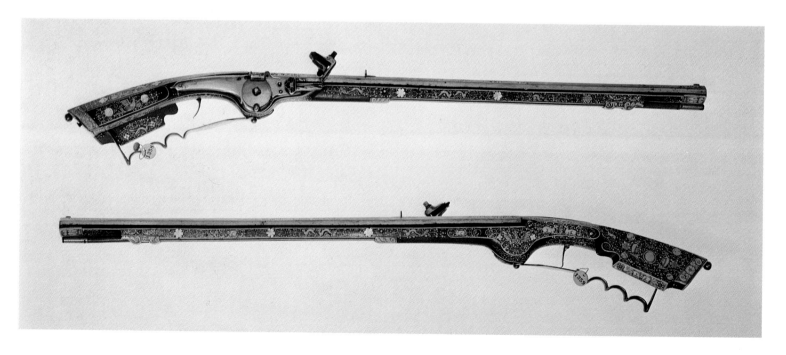

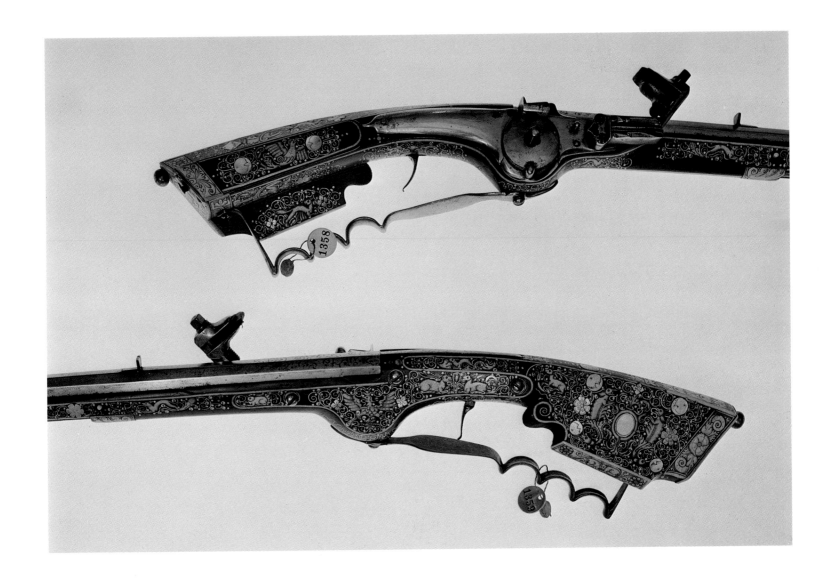

87 *Pair of Wheel-lock Pistols*

SILESIAN (TESCHEN), *ca. 1660*

THE full cherry stocks are inlaid with engraved staghorn and mother-of-pearl. The breech quarter of the barrels is octagonal and makes a gradual transition to round. The unidentified maker's stamp PK is struck in the crudely engraved breech section, which was gilded originally. The locks have flush wheels retained by a narrow iron ring. Their dog springs are internal, and there is a button release for the pancover. The simple iron triggerguards (one is replaced), which also were gilded, extend forward entirely over the bulge of the stock. Their pointed forward terminals are abruptly angled to enter the stock. The pommels are encircled by an engraved and gilded iron band that retains an engraved staghorn plaque.

The design and execution of the stock inlay is very closely related to that of the Tschinke and probably reflects the Eastern European origin of these pistols. The butt and pommel are associated with those of South German flintlock pistols that existed contemporaneously (see Schedelmann, *Die grossen Büchsenmacher*, pl. 21).

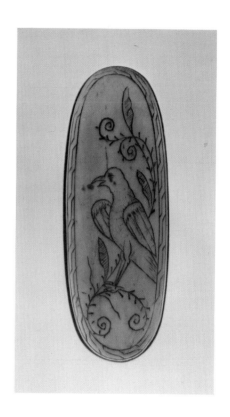

Provenance: Holland and Holland, London, 1970.
Overall length, 27¼ in. (69.2 cm.); barrel, 19½ in. (49.5 cm.); caliber, .50

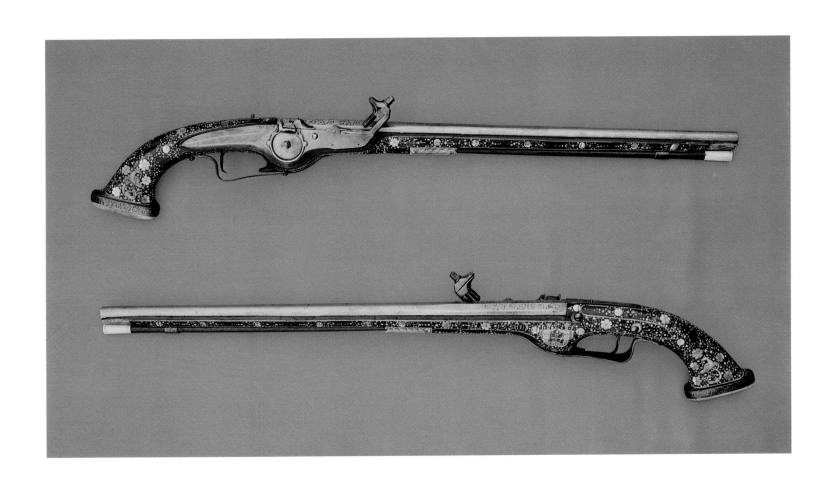

88 *Swedish Snaplock Rifle*

SWEDISH (STOCKHOLM), dated 1722

THE full walnut stock, lightly carved with foliage and inlaid with pierced and engraved brass plaques, terminates in a horn forend cap. Engraved among the decoration of the cheekpiece is the inscription SCHERTIGER FECIT 1722. To the rear of this decoration an engraved brass flower conceals the push-button release for the butt-trap cover. On the forend between the triggerguard and the rear ramrod pipe is inlaid an engraved brass figure of Diana. The full octagonal barrel, rifled with eight grooves, tapers and flares slightly at the muzzle. It has an engraved border at the breech and is fitted with an iron bar rear sight and a brass blade foresight. The lock, with flat surfaces, has border and foliage engraving. The steel face of the battery swivels to the side to form a safety. Three diamond-faceted ramrod pipes hold the rod, and an iron ground ball protects the heel of the brass buttplate. The brass triggerguard terminates in foliate finials and has two indented finger rests in the grip rail. Its exaggerated inward curve results from undue pressure on the grip rail, which has also drawn the rear support from its original almost vertical position.

The only signature appearing on this arm is that of the gunstocker Jonas Schertiger the younger of Stockholm (d. 1748). The elder (d. 1715) had been appointed royal gunstocker in 1692, a position that his son apparently never achieved. Stockholm gunstockers belonged to the guild of cabinetmakers rather than to that of gunmakers, and records of litigation between the two organizations are common. In 1745 the younger Schertiger was involved in one of these litigations for having accused certain pistolsmiths of stocking guns, and was in turn accused by them of producing finished guns in his shop against guild regulations.

The peculiar Swedish snaplock represents a national style and tradition that existed contemporaneously in Sweden with the French flintlock. This example shows the assimilation of elements of current French style in its flat surfaces, border engraving, design of its battery spring, and the shape of its top jaw screw. The buttstock's overall form is associated with the Silesian hind's foot Tschinke stock, while its heavy proportions come from the German cheekstock.

The accompanying powder horn is Norwegian. It is crudely carved with scenes depicting biblical and epic themes, and is thrice dated 1713.

Provenance: Sotheby (William G. Renwick Collection, Pt. I), July 17, 1972, lot 2.
Overall length, 43⅜ in. (117.8 cm.); barrel, 35½ in. (90 cm.); caliber, .42

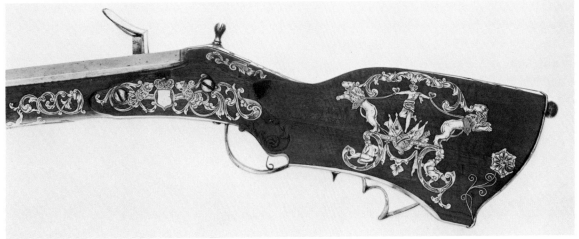

89 *Flintlock Pistol*

DANISH, dated 1738

THE stump walnut stock is relief carved with foliage, borders, and moldings, and terminates in a horn tip. The barrel has a chiseled panel on the upper breech, and a raised sighting rib extends nearly to the muzzle with an iron blade front sight. The flintlock with convex surfaces is chiseled within panels and is signed below the battery spring, VAL: MARR A COPPENHAGEN. The mounts, of chased silvered white brass, include an escutcheon with the arms of the Danish branch of the von Eickstedt family. The inside of the trigger-guard bow has the Copenhagen control mark with the date 1738, the mark of the sword cutler Johan Christian Weidenhaupt, the state inspector's mark of Peter Nicolai von Haven, and the fish stamp for the month February 18 to March 3. Two pipes hold the original wooden horn-tipped ramrod.

Valentin Marr, born in Zella in Thuringia in 1696, apparently apprenticed in his native Germany, but subsequently spent two years (1727–1729) as a journeyman in Sweden under David Bars. After a brief return to Zella, he departed permanently for Copenhagen (1732), where he was to spend the remainder of his long life (d. 1786). He soon became court gunsmith to King Christian VI after having presented a pair of pistols mounted in mother-of-pearl to the king.

In combination with the date of the mounts, the arms on the escutcheon show that this pistol can have belonged to only two members of the von Eickstedt family: either Hans Henrick, minister of state and tutor of King Frederik VI when he was crown prince, who in 1738 was a captain in the 3rd Jutland National Cavalry Regiment; or his brother, Alexander Ernst von Eickstedt, a lieutenant of cavalry stationed near Copenhagen.

Much of the ornament of this pistol relates to designs published by Nicolas Guérard in the early eighteenth century that are combined with a few rococo elements. However, the convex lock surfaces are survivals of a French fashion of the late seventeenth century. These convex forms, discarded in Paris at the turn of the century, were favored by German gunmakers as well as by the Dutch and English and continued in use through the first decades of the eighteenth century.

Provenance: Emil Buchel, Berlin-Spandau, 1930; Stephen V. Grancsay, Brooklyn, New York, 1970.
Overall length, 17¾ in. (45 cm.); barrel, 11¾ in. (29.8 cm.); caliber, .58

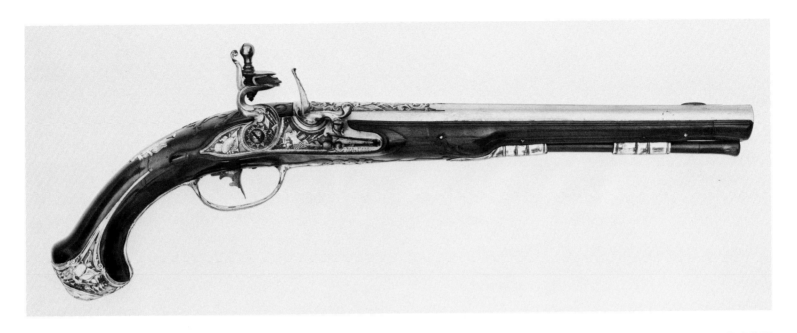

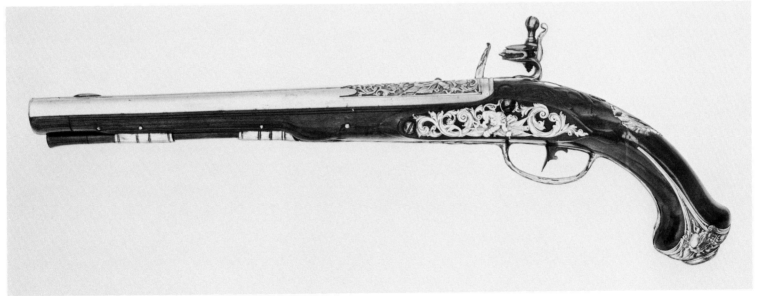

90 *Snaphaunce Rifle*

RUSSIAN (MOSCOW?), ca. 1680

THE fruitwood full stock is inlaid with engraved ivory plaques, and the entire cheekpiece is decorated with pierced and sculptured ivory figures and foliate designs; a sculptured grotesque monster serves as the ramrod entry pipe near the muzzle. The forend is fitted with two brass sling swivels, and the buttstock terminates in an ivory buttplate protected by four ground balls. The full octagonal barrel is tapered and flared and is rifled with six grooves. A narrow engraved band decorates the breech, and a series of punched dots surrounds the bore on the face of the muzzle. The rear post sight and the front blade are both of iron. The snaphaunce lock has at a later date been fitted with a sear and tumbler of the French flintlock type. It is chiseled in high relief, engraved, and parcel gilt. The striking face of the battery is a separate piece dovetailed to the body and retained by a screw; the cock buffer is sculptured in the shape of a lion. The iron mounts include the triggerguard with three finger rests on the grip rail and two sling swivels on the forend.

This is an excellent example of a seventeenth-century Russian firearm since it embodies many interesting sculptural details on both lock and stock. Like most Russian arms of this period, it combines Western European academic design with a local folk art approach. This is most apparent in the relief carving of the overlay of the cheekpiece. This design is a composite of Western elements from the early seventeenth century, mid-century baroque, and classical details from its final quarter. The central scene depicting a monkey teasing two dogs with an urn dangling from ribbons derives directly from a plate in the French pattern book of Thomas Picquot (1638). The framed surround, crowded with foliage and containing birds, is also typical of the Picquot style. The suggestive half-nude couples—the men playing with the women's skirts—reflects Western European baroque. The pair of trumpeting cherubs and the Roman warrior are elements commonly found in French published patterns from the later years of the seventeenth century, and the lion and griffin are heraldic figures referred to by Tarassuk on Kremlin Armory pistols of precisely this period.[1] Forward of the cheekpiece and between the lock screws an engraved ivory inlay—half-woman, half winged serpent—appears to come from the sideplate design on pl. 9 of François Marcou's 1657 pattern book.

Western elements appear in a similar unusual combination on the lock, where they are also given the same local character as those on the cheekpiece. The design of the cock seems to have been directly influenced by a cock in an unnumbered plate from Jean Bérain's pattern book of 1659, although the winged grotesque figure has been transferred from the breast of the cock to the rear, its wings thus forming the top jaw support. A similar positioning of a like figure with different details may be found in pl. 14 of Marcou. Also typical of the Bérain patterns and period are the turnings of the top jaw screw and the two opposing volutes on the cock jaws. The top jaw in the form of an animal head and the grotesque animal head forming the lockplate terminal are designs that were popular in Europe a decade earlier than the Bérain book.

The presence of such a substantial number of pattern book

---

[1] Leonid Tarassuk, *Russian Pistols in the Seventeenth Century* (York, Pa.: George Shumway, 1968), p. 26.

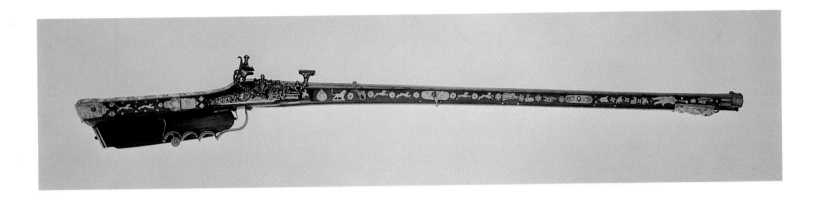

elements on this arm is beyond coincidence and seems to indicate that the gunsmith had access to several seventeenth-century French pattern books. The indiscriminate use of patterns of various periods, whose interpretation is unconventional, is testimony to the strength of native folk art tradition. Here, no pattern book elements have been accepted verbatim as they were in many Western European countries with closer cultural affinity to France. Dr. Tarassuk has pointed out the influence of folk art of the Russian North—especially bone carving—on Moscow arms decorators. He has also pointed out the presence of pattern books in the Kremlin workshops.[2]

The snaphaunce lock was used extensively on Moscow firearms in the seventeenth century. Its plate follows one or the other of two wheel-lock forms: pistols usually have a deep, semicircular bulge to the lower profile, while guns have the form illustrated here. The separately faced battery is also found on sixteenth-century German snaphaunces.

The buttstock is also of German rifle form, but it has been substantially lengthened to make a shoulder stock of that which in Germany was intended to be fired from the cheek. This extension is found not only on Russian longarms, but also on earlier Polish and Lithuanian wheel-lock rifles.

Provenance: Sotheby (William G. Renwick Collection, Pt. III), March 19, 1973, lot 48; Frank E. Bivens, Los Angeles, California, 1976.
Overall length, 53⅝ in. (136 cm.); barrel, 39⅛ in. (99.5 cm.); caliber, .32

---

[2] Ibid., p. 33.

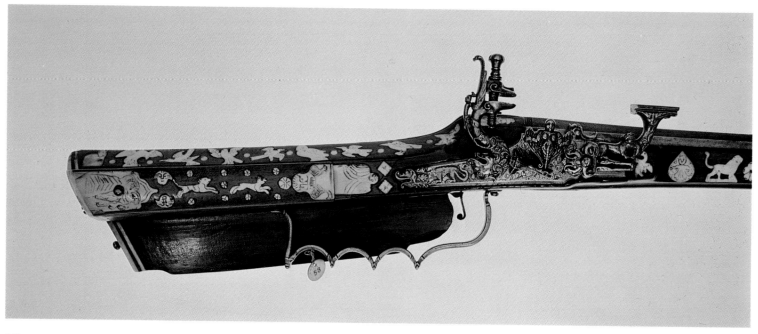

90

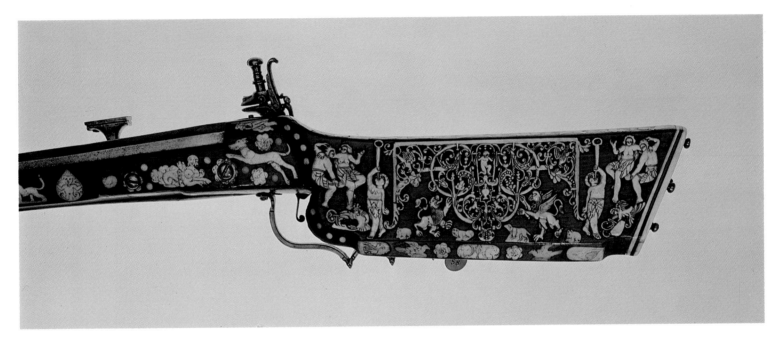

90

91 *Flintlock Gun*

RUSSIAN (TULA?), ca.1795

THE stump walnut full stock is inlaid with engraved gilt brass plaques and silver wire and ends in a horn forend cap. It is carved with relief borders and a raised checkpiece and has a checkered grip. The barrel has a hooked breech and is finished in four stages: the breech has two side flats and a relief-chiseled central panel; following this are two short sections, one sixteen-sided, one round; forward of these the barrel continues sixteen-sided to the ring muzzle. The gold inscription *M. Ivan Soushkin* [*sic*] in a combination of roman and cyrillic characters is inlaid along the top breech flat. The remaining engraved gold and silver inlay includes the imperial eagle surrounding the silver blade front sight. The touch hole is platinum lined. The lock has flat surfaces, a rainproof pan, and a roller on the battery spring. It is engraved with borders and scrolls and is inlaid with engraved silver and gold floral designs. The same gold inscription as on the barrel is repeated on the lockplate. The blued iron mounts are also inlaid with silver and gold. The finial is missing from the original ramrod.

Ivan Pushkin is known from his signature on arms in the Kremlin and other collections. The peculiar spelling of his name on this barrel indicates that it was finished by a Western European, a number of whom are known to have been working in Russian shops at that time. When this piece was sold on July 25, 1960, the Sotheby's catalogue description suggested incorrectly that the artisan may have been of Croatian origin.

This gun, like the majority of those of eighteenth-century Russian manufacture, mirrors multinational European styles incorporating various time periods. The style of the buttplate derives from French mid-century prototypes, while its latest features are the rainproof pan and roller battery spring which derive from English arms of the 1780s and 1790s.

Provenance: Sotheby, July 25, 1960, lot 143; A. R. Dufty, Farnham, England.
Overall length, 48 in. (122 cm.); barrel, 31⅝ in. (80.2 cm.); caliber, .79

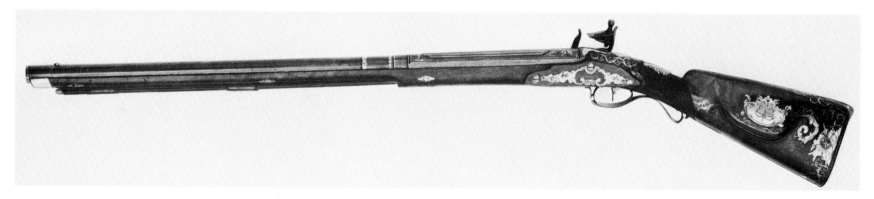

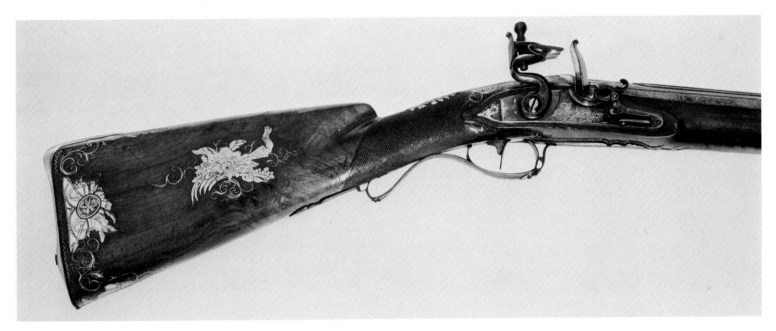

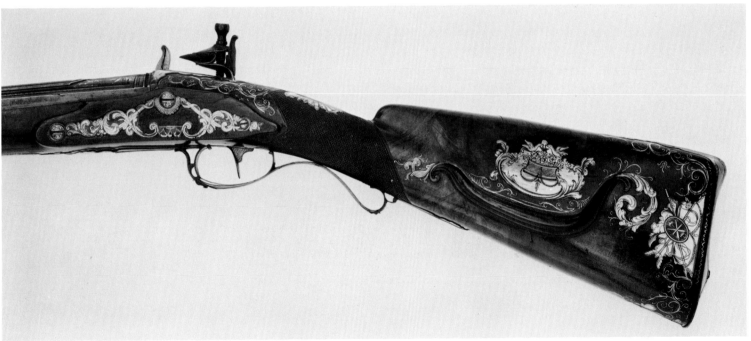

92 Cased Percussion Six-Barreled Pistol

AMERICAN (NORWICH, CONNECTICUT), 1842–1847

THE six revolving browned barrels are mounted on a blued iron frame. They are separated by concave ribs, one of which is stamped PATENTED 1837 CAST STEEL, the other, TRYON. The double action is housed within the frame; a ring trigger activates the bar hammer that is stamped ALLEN & THURBER NORWICH C-T. The frame and flash guard and barrel breeches are fully engraved, and the plain ivory grips have a blank German silver escutcheon.

The rosewood case has German silver reinforced corners and a blank German silver escutcheon in the lid. It is lined with faded red velvet and contains the following accessories: a rosewood ramrod and cleaning rod, both with turned ivory handles; an ivory-handled screwdriver; a steel flask with German silver mounts and compartments for balls and caps; a steel bullet mold with a blued sprue cutter; a ball puller; a worm; and a powder measure. There are two covered compartments.

The firm of brothers-in-law Ethan Allen and Charles Thurber was first established in Grafton, Massachusetts. In 1842 it was moved to Norwich, Connecticut, where it remained until 1847, when it was again moved, this time to Worcester, Massachusetts. The date on this piece refers to Allen's patent of the first practical self-cocking system. Its application to a revolving arm enabled the firm to produce the fastest firing smallarm of the day.

The style of the engraving is baroque revival with the addition of a few neoclassical borders. The engraving of the frame and flash guard is in low relief that was produced by reducing the background with random hatching.

The name Tryon on the barrel rib probably indicates that this set was marketed by the Philadelphia firm of Tryon and Co. which was founded in 1829. Established as a gun manufactory, after 1836 the firm carried on a considerable mercantile trade that gradually replaced its gunmaking.

Provenance: Norm Flayderman, New Milford, Connecticut.
Overall length, 7⅛ in. (18 cm.); barrel, 3¼ in. (8.2 cm.); caliber, .31

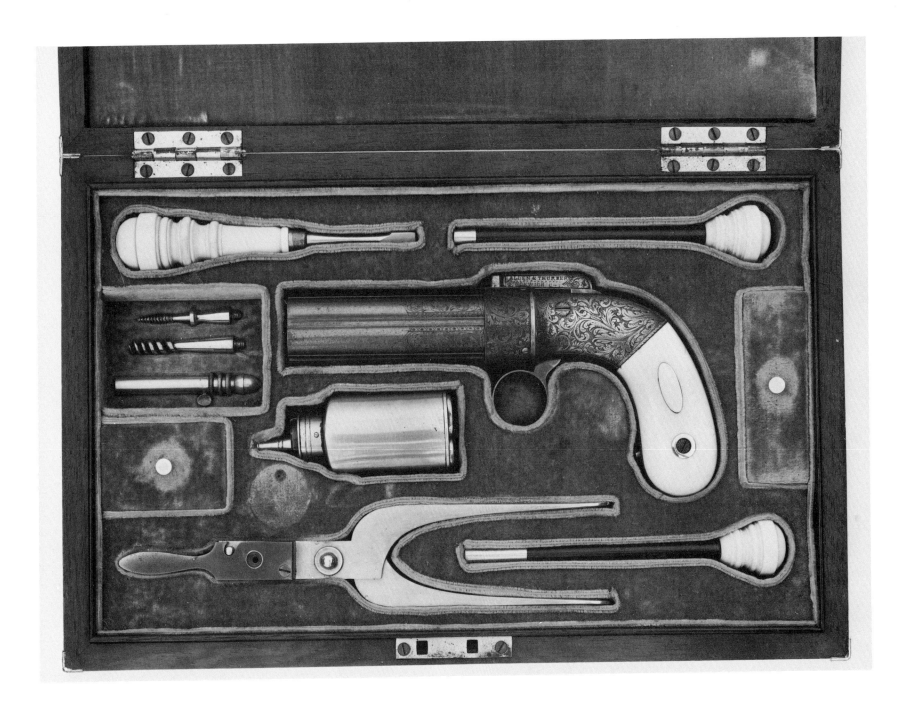

93 *Cased Cartridge Repeating Rifle*

AMERICAN (NEW HAVEN, CONNECTICUT), 1870

THE two-piece stock has a butt of crotch walnut and a plain walnut forend. The full octagonal blued barrel is fitted with an adjustable iron open rear sight and an iron foresight. On the upper flat at the breech is stamped the inscription WINCHESTER'S REPEATING ARMS, NEW HAVEN, CT. KING'S IMPROVEMENT—PATENTED—MARCH 29, 1866, OCTOBER 16, 1860. The gilt brass receiver houses the lever action, which cocks the hammer and loads the chamber. It is engraved overall, and the loading gate on its right side is blued. To the rear of the loading gate is engraved the name Guillermo Crespo within a riband, and on the opposite side are the crowned arms of Spain. The hammer and trigger have case-hardened colors; the lever and screws are blued. On the frame under the lever is the serial number 36174; this indicates that it was produced in 1870. The forend cap and buttplate are of gilt brass. There are two sling swivels.

The rosewood case has brass protected corners and a German silver escutcheon in the center of the lid engraved with the initials G.C. It is lined with blue velvet and has compartments for cartridge boxes as well as individual cartridges. There is a covered compartment for accessories.

The model 1866 rifle was the first arm to be manufactured under the Winchester name. Oliver Winchester, a stockholder in the Volcanic Repeating Firearms Company, bought the company following its bankruptcy in 1857. He first produced a successful and popular rifle designed by B. Tyler Henry in 1860. The Henry rifle, improved and modified by Nelson King, became the 1866 Winchester. The Volcanic, Henry, and Winchester were lever-action arms. However, the Winchester was by far the most popular of the three since the loading gate was in the action rather than at the muzzle as in the earlier two.

The engraving on this rifle is attributed to L. D. Nimschke, who decorated many of the finest Winchester arms, and his initials appear on the receiver. The style of engraving is characteristic of the Victorian period, being composed of a combination of baroque and rococo revival elements in a crowded composition. A few neoclassical elements are also included, and the riband with its zig-zag borders bearing the owner's name derives from the "Bérain" style of the first quarter of the eighteenth century. The advent of the machine age did not obviate the need for highly decorated firearms, although from this time on the decorative emphasis seems to have been on the metalwork rather than on the stock.

The owner, Guillermo Crespo, has not been identified. The crowned arms of Spain on the receiver, and the quality of the arm itself, certainly imply that this rifle was intended for royal presentation.

Provenance: Glode Requa, New York City, 1963.
Overall length, 44 in. (111 cm.); caliber, .44 rim fire
Length of case, 46 in. (117.5 cm.); width, 10½ in. (26.8 cm.)

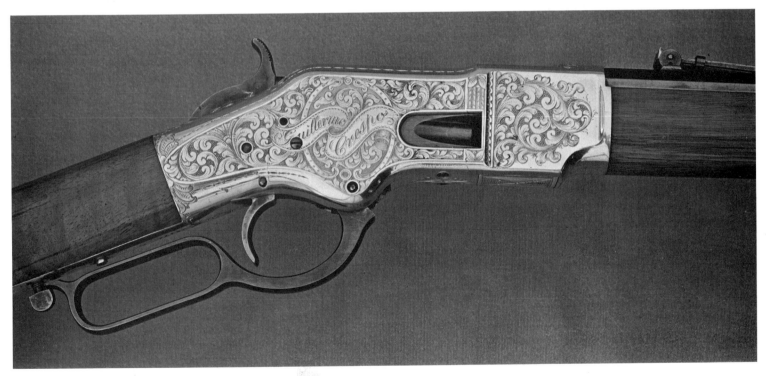

94 *Cartridge Shotgun*

AMERICAN (ILION, NEW YORK), ca. 1870

THE two-piece stock consists of a plain stump walnut butt and forend. The browned sixteen-gauge damascus barrel has a raised sighting rib that terminates in a bead sight. It is decorated with gold inlay at the breech and at the muzzle. The rear portion of the sighting rib has the gold inscription E. REMINGTON & SONS ILION NEW YORK, U.S.A.; Liège proof marks are struck under the barrel breech. The frame, rolling block, hammer, and triggerguard are gold inlaid en suite with the barrel. An engraved inlaid scene of a dog and a quail appears on either side of the frame, and the Great Seal of the United States is engraved and inlaid in low relief on top of the receiver. The name REMINGTON is inlaid in gold on the upper tang of the action. The buttplate, forend cap, and two ramrod pipes are also decorated en suite. The buttplate is fitted with a hinged trap, and there is an ebonized rosewood-tipped ramrod.

The Remington Arms Company was one of the principal arms manufactories in the United States by the middle of the nineteenth century. Its founder, Eliphalet Remington, began a one-man gunsmithing business at Ilion, New York, early in the second quarter of the nineteenth century. By the time of his death in 1861, the firm, under his three sons, was able to expand extensively to handle large Civil War contracts. Two designs patented by the company—the revolver, a marked improvement over the Colt, and the rolling block single shot rifle and shotgun action—won international acclaim.

The rolling block action used on this piece was invented about 1862 by Leonard M. Geiger, who was subsequently employed by the factory. It was then modified and improved,

resulting in the action seen here which first appeared in 1866 or 1867. Minor changes made over the years produced four different model variations, of which the first is known as the Number 1 or large rolling block. While the rolling block was normally used on rifles, the Number 1 action was fitted to 16 and 20 gauge shotguns between 1867 and 1892.[1]

The gun illustrated is of presentation quality; however, this does not account for certain variations from the Number 1 action arms of standard manufacture. Significantly different are the separate triggerguard, the lack of the breech block-hammer pin retainer plate, and the lines and generous proportions of the buttstock. Moreover, the design of the gold inlay shows a close affinity with European decorative work. The clue to these differences is to be found in the Liège proofmarks on the barrel. A gun of identical construction—although more fully marked—examined by the authors bears Liège marks not only on the barrel but on the receiver and rolling block as well, and the full patent inscription and New York address are stamped on the top tang of the frame. The obvious conclusion is that these two arms were produced in Liège under contract to Remington. It should be noted that these "contract" arms are of superior quality and are more decorative than the normal Remington line. Undoubtedly, the Belgian shops produced the custom order deluxe arms. On this piece, the engraving of the Great Seal is inferior to the remainder of the engraving and inlay on the rest of the arm.

---

[1] Frank de Haas, *Single Shot Rifles and Actions* (Chicago: Gun Digest, 1969), p. 53.

Provenance: L. C. Jackson, Dallas, Texas, 1962.
Overall length, 46½ in. (118 cm.); barrel, 30 in. (76.2 cm.); gauge,
16

APPENDIX

Gunstock Woods

THE identification and classification of gunstock woods has been largely neglected in works on antique firearms. Only in books on modern firearms is there any knowledgeable and serious attempt to identify and classify the types of woods used in stocks. This attention given the subject in modern books probably results from the prospective owner having to choose the stock wood for a custom-made gun. This is a situation not encountered by the firearms collector, who is dealing with arms already produced. Moreover, many of these modern books are written by active gunsmiths who are not only confronted with the choice of the various types of woods and cuts, but who also are familiar with their strengths and weaknesses. Despite this, some cuts go unclassified, while other woods which were popular in the seventeenth or eighteenth centuries are no longer used.

Our objective in this brief introduction to the subject is to point out some of the major types of woods and cuts that were popular from the sixteenth through the nineteenth centuries. Identification of wood species by microanalysis is a very accurate science today. However, in this study none of the examples in the collection has been identified by this method. All the identification of wood types and species has been done by visual inspection, which obviously has its pitfalls; fruitwoods are the most difficult to identify specifically. The types of cuts can only be determined by close inspection and familiarity with the various parts of the tree from which stocks were cut. The terminology of cuts defined here emphasizes the artistic qualities of the wood, its figure and coloration, rather than the technical aspects of its cutting.

During the three centuries covered by this work many types of gunstock woods were used. However, during certain periods and on certain types of arms, specific woods were employed. From the early sixteenth century through the middle of the seventeenth fruitwoods were by far the most common for stocking. Wheel-lock stocks are usually of cherry and sometimes of apple and pear. The use of fruitwoods extended into the early flintlock arms, snaphaunces, and miquelet lock guns. From the mid-seventeenth century until the present, walnut became universal for use in gunstocks. The use of walnut seems to have occurred in Italy first on early seventeenth-century wheel-lock arms. It then became popular on French flintlocks and spread internationally through that arm's use. During the latter half of the seventeenth century until the early part of the eighteenth maple became an alternate to walnut. In Spain maple enjoyed very limited use, but cherry stocks, artificially grained to resemble maple, were popular well into the eighteenth century. Also, in the United States maple continued in use through the nineteenth century.

Fruitwoods, which dominated the stocking of wheel-locks, were usually straight grained and offered a fine background for the traditional engraved staghorn inlay. Fruitwoods were sometimes ebonized, and in the latter part of the seventeenth century they were occasionally arificially grained to resemble figured maple. They were dense, durable woods, and, when carved, their close grain produced a very crisp effect. Cherry was dominant, although apple and pear were occasionally used.

Walnut, unlike fruitwoods, was chosen for the effect of its decorative grain. Several types of figured grain can be cut from the walnut tree, the most common being stump and crotch. During the seventeenth century stump walnut stocks were quite popular. This wood is described in des Granges's contract of 1668 as "marbled."[1] Modern writers often refer to it as "root walnut," but the wood itself actually comes from the main body of the stump. The multicolored or marbled effect in this wood is quite obvious in the pictured section of a walnut stump (Fig. 1). Also, the highly figured (curled grain) areas are visible, and in the lower center may be seen root knots that have been enveloped by the growing tree. Several have drying checks, and to the right of center

is a long crevice containing ingrown bark and trapped soil. These flaws, common to this type of wood, are often found in finished stocks filled with glued-in blocks of similar wood (see No. 13). A fine example of figured and marbled stump wood may be seen in the buttstock of the Hess fowler (No. 64).

Crotch walnut had limited use prior to the nineteenth century. It comes from the center cut through the fork of the tree. The figure is confined to the angle of the juncture and has the form of a long, tapered feather (Fig. 2). A good example of crotch walnut is the stock of the Michele Battista gun (No. 75).

The maple used in the latter part of the seventeenth cen-

Figure 1

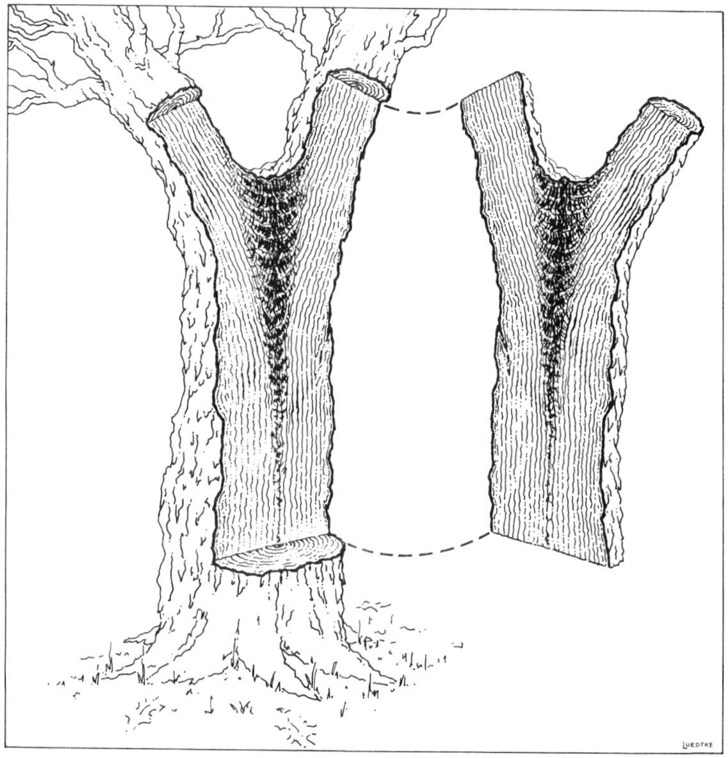

Figure 2

[1] Lenk, *Flintlock*, p. 178.

tury was usually burl. It is probably the least recognized of any of the stock woods, being often identified as root or "burr" walnut. It is heavily figured and very close grained. While usually stained dark, red or yellow undertones distinguish it from the more open-grained, darkly colored walnut. Contrary to popular belief, the burl does not come from the root. Rather, it is found at random on the trunk of the tree, where it appears as a large wartlike growth. The tree illustrated (Fig. 3) has many such burls. Figure 4 shows a section of such a burl with a pistol stock blank cut from it. The rough lower section has its bark removed to reveal the hundreds of tiny buds that make up the burl. The three dark spots in the sideplate area of the blank are encapsulated pieces of bark. They are occasionally found patched in finished stocks. Burl maple stocks were tremendously popular in London, principally during the reign of William III. Their highly contrasting colors distinguish them from stocks of more uniform color made on the Continent, and probably result from a different staining technique. Use of burl maple died out in the first quarter of the eighteenth century.

Curly maple—sometimes called "fiddleback" because of its use in the violin—has a wavy grain and, when it is found, comes from the main trunk of the tree. It was used in Germany as an alternate to burl maple. It dominated gunstocking in the United States from the colonial period to the nineteenth century, and is characteristic of the long rifle.

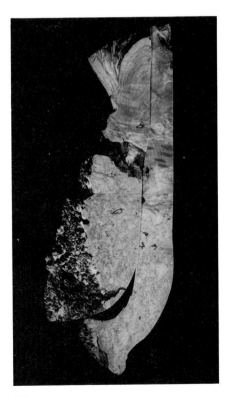

Figure 3

Figure 4

BIBLIOGRAPHY

Blackmore, Howard L. *Guns and Rifles of the World*. New York: Viking Press, 1965.

————. *Hunting Weapons*. London: Barrie & Jenkins, 1971.

Blair, Claude. *Arms, Armour and Base-Metalwork: The James A. de Rothschild Collection at Waddesdon Manor*. Fribourg: Published for the National Trust by Office du Livre, 1974.

————. *European & American Arms, c. 1100–1850*. London: B. T. Batsford, 1962.

————. *Pistols of the World*. New York: Viking Press, 1968.

Carpegna, Nolfo di. *Armi da Fuoco della Collezione Odescalchi*. Rome: Marte, 1968.

Fiosconi, Cesar, and Guserio, Jordam. *Espingarda Perfeyta* [*The Perfect Gun*]. 1718. Edited and translated by Rainer Daehnhardt and W. Keith Neal. Facsimile reprint. London: Sotheby Parke Bernet, 1974.

George, J. N. *English Pistols & Revolvers: An Historical Outline of the Development and Design of English Hand Firearms from the 17th Century to the Present Day*. 1938. Reprint. New York: Arco Publishing Co., 1962.

Graells, Eudald. *Les armes de foc de Ripoll*. Ripoll: Impremta Maideu, 1974.

Grancsay, Stephen V., ed. *Master French Gunsmiths' Designs of the XVII–XIX Centuries, Reproduced in Facsimile*. New York: Winchester Press, 1970.

Hayward, J. F. *The Art of the Gunmaker*. I: *1500–1660*. II: *1660–1830*. New York: St. Martin's Press, 1962, 1963.

————. *European Firearms*. London: H. M. Stationery Office, 1955.

Hoff, Arne. *Feuerwaffen*. 2 vols. Braunschweig: Klinkhardt & Biermann, 1969.

Jackson, Herbert J. *European Hand Firearms of the Sixteenth, Seventeenth & Eighteenth Centuries*. 2nd ed. London: The Holland Press, 1959.

Lavin, James D. *A History of Spanish Firearms*. London: Herbert Jenkins, 1965.

Lenk, Torsten. *The Flintlock: its origin and development*. Translated by G. A. Urquart. Edited by J. F. Hayward. London: The Holland Press, 1965.

Metropolitan Museum of Art. *Early Firearms of Great Britain and Ireland from the Collection of Clay P. Bedford*. Greenwich, Conn.: New York Graphic Society, 1971.

Neal, W. Keith. *Spanish Guns and Pistols*. London: G. Bell & Sons, 1955.

————, and Back, D. H. L. *Great British Gunmakers, 1740–1790: The History of John Twigg and the Packington Guns*. London: Sotheby Parke Bernet, 1975.

Peterson, Harold L. *Arms and Armor in Colonial America, 1526–1783*. Harrisburg, Pa.: Stackpole Co., 1956.

Schedelmann, Hans. *Die grossen Büchsenmacher*. Braunschweig: Klinkhardt & Biermann, 1972.

Støckel, Johan F. *Haandskydevaabens bedømmelse I–II*. Copenhagen: Nordlundes Bogrrykkeri, 1938–1943.

Tarassuk, L. *Antique European and American Firearms at the Hermitage Museum*. Translated by R. Drapkin. Leningrad: Iskusstvo Publishing House, 1971.

Terenzi, Marcello. *Gli Armaioli Anghiaresi nei Secoli XVIII e XIX*. Rome: Marte, 1968.

Wallace Collection, London. *European Arms and Armour*. I: *Armour*. II: *Arms*. Edited by Sir James Mann. London: Printed for the Trustees by William Clowes and Sons, 1962.

Wilkinson, Frederick. *Small Arms*. New York: Hawthorne Books, 1965.

Winant, Lewis. *Early Percussion Firearms: A History of Early Percussion Firearms Ignition—from Forsyth to Winchester .44/40*. New York: William Morrow, 1959.

INDEX

DECORATED FIREARMS, 1540–1870,
FROM THE COLLECTION OF CLAY P. BEDFORD
was composed in Granjon type by Heritage Printers, Inc., Charlotte,
North Carolina, and was printed by Lebanon Valley Offset Company,
Inc., Annville, Pennsylvania, on Kashmir dull coated paper. Binding
was done by Haddon Craftsmen, Inc., Scranton, Pennsylvania. Richard
Stinely designed the book.